**COMBAT AND SURVIVAL**

WHAT IT TAKES TO FIGHT AND WIN

VOLUME
26

Originally published in the United Kingdom in weekly parts **COMBAT & SURVIVAL** is a study of the armed forces at work. It shows the skills taught to soldiers and the way in which military units operate. It examines the weapons and equipment used by different armies; and, by looking at recruit training and exercises, **COMBAT & SURVIVAL** demonstrates how the armed forces develop individual responsibility, leadership and initiative.

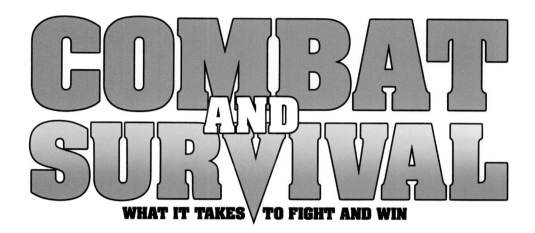

# COMBAT AND SURVIVAL

### WHAT IT TAKES TO FIGHT AND WIN

## VOLUME
## 26

H. S. STUTTMAN, INC. *publishers*          Westport, Connecticut 06889

# Contents

## Volume 26

**Combat Skills**

Infantry Skills No. 22: Sentry Duties — 1505
Infantry Skills No. 23: Taking Prisoners — 1511
Infantry Skills No. 24: Tactical Questioning — 1517

**NBC Survival**

No. 9: First Aid for Blood and Choking Agents — 1522
No. 10: First Aid for Blister Agent — 1524
No. 11: First Aid for Mental Incapacitants — 1526

**Weapons and Equipment Guide**

No. 75: Snap Shooting with the Steyr — 1528
No. 76: Marauding with the Marder — 1534
No. 77: Blasting with the Blooper: The M79 Grenade Launcher — 1540

**Survival**

Body Armour No. 1: Protect Yourself with Body Armour — 1546
Body Armour No. 2: Special Forces Personal Protection — 1550
Camouflage and Concealment: Personal Camouflage and Concealment — 1554

**Fighting Fit**

French Marine Commandos: Hitting the Beach — 1558
RAF Mountain Rescue: Into the Hills — 1562

**Combat Reports**

Zanzibar: Quelling the Riots Part 1 — 1510
Zanzibar: Quelling the Riots Part 2 — 1516
Lebanon: Bodyguards in Beirut — 1561

Published by H. S. STUTTMAN INC.
Westport, Connecticut 06889
© Aerospace Publishing 1991
ISBN 0-87475-560-3

# Combat Skills

# SENTRY DUTIES

*"War is 99 per cent waiting for something to happen, and one per cent fighting."* This may be an exaggeration, but there's no doubt that the greatest part of your time in war will be spent preparing and planning for battle, waiting for the enemy, or recovering from an engagement.

Sometimes you will be able to rest or relax but, to do this safely, someone must be alert and looking after your interests. The importance of the sentry's job cannot be overstated. Lives of comrades depend upon the alertness and efficiency of just one man.

### Thorough briefing

A sentry needs clear orders. He will face complicated situations and may have to make difficult decisions. So when you are briefing a sentry, omit nothing, leave nothing to chance and make sure nothing can be misunderstood. And if you are a sentry, make sure you understand your orders, that you know what to do if your post is approached by a person or a vehicle, and that you know how to raise the alarm.

If you are close to the enemy you also need to know the direction from which he is most likely to approach; where your neighbouring sentry posts are and the signal for them to fire defensive fire; the name of forward landmarks; and, most important of all,

## 7 POINTS FOR SENTRY DUTY

1. **Sentries should be posted in pairs.**
2. **Check sentries regularly**
3. **Know when to expect the return of friendly patrols.**
4. **Observe your arc from a good fire position.**
5. **If you are using lighting, make sure you do not illuminate your own positions.**
6. **Do not talk in tactical sentry positions.**
7. **Concentrate all the time: a dozy sentry is a danger to the whole unit.**

*Whenever you halt for any period of time, no matter how small your unit, you will always put out a sentry of some kind. Sentry duties are an essential feature of every type of military operation and their importance cannot be overestimated.*

*Left: On exercise the sentry duty is sometimes seen as a tedious inconvenience, but in wartime every unit will be vulnerable to attack, even when far behind the front line.*

*Right: Adequately briefed and alert sentries will prevent your unit falling victim to this type of attack. Sentries should never be deployed singly or in a position where they cannot cover all the approaches to that position.*

## NBC SENTRY

An NBC sentry must know:

1. The prevailing situation – what the enemy's intentions are regarding chemical attack.
2. His mission – i.e. to warn of an NBC attack within five seconds so that Chemical Immediate Action Drill can be carried out.
3. When his tour of duty starts and ends.
4. What his location will be during his tour.
5. When an attack occurs, to:
   * sound the alarm
   * check his detector paper and, if there is a colour change, report it
   * report the development of the attack on the radio

* change detector paper every minute until no further colour change occurs, then inform the unit commander.
6. What new position to take up if the wind changes direction.
7. What to do about chemical delivery by mist, smoke, falling droplets.
8. Action to be taken against low-flying aircraft or suspicious persons.
9. To whom he should report and where they are.
10. Nicknames or codewords.
11. Passwords and passnumbers.

# THE NEED FOR VIGILANCE

*In the run-up to the major conflict in Europe, key points such as communications centres, nuclear delivery systems and airfields, will probably be attacked by Warsaw Pact Special Forces. They may dress in our uniforms and those of our NATO allies, so do not relax your guard at the first sign of familiar British DPM. Here the Spetsnaz go into action against a NATO airfield.*

**Security lighting**
Security lighting must be very carefully used. Lights should illuminate the areas to be guarded and not the guards. They must not create areas of shadow through which the enemy could move undetected.

**Length of stag**
Stags should not be over one hour in length. Attention usually starts to go downhill after 20 minutes. Changeover should be staggered so that one sentry goes off duty on the hour and the other on the half hour, so one sentry has always got night vision and is fully alert.

**Dogs**
Dogs are excellent for warning of a break-in a can be used in a dog r between the inner and perimeter fencing. The should not be relied or the sentry work for yo they are vulnerable to own, but they do great increase the amount o ground one sentry can cover.

**The limit of sound, smell and vision**
In a tactical environment such as a patrol harbour sentries should be placed beyond the range at which the presence of the unit is detectable by sight, sound or smell, whichever is further. During a work phase there will obviously be more noise, so it may be necessary to push the sentries out further while you prepare the position and bring them in again when work is complete.

**Covert and overt sentry positions**
When guarding a facility, it is a good idea to put an OP screen further out to supplement the men on the gates and mobile perimeter patrols. OPs can give advance warning of enemy approach or suspicious movement.

**Guard commander**
Sentries must be regularly checked by the guard or unit commander to make sure they are alert and doing their job. They should have weapons in the shoulder and be looking out over their arc of responsibility.

**Communication cor**
A pull cord from the ser position to the back-up position can be effectiv long as the line is tied t arm or leg of the back-u sentry and nobody trips it, creating a false alarm

the details of friendly patrols that may return through or near your post.

### Use the password

In addition to all this, you must know the password. At night it is not always possible to identify someone approaching your position until they are dangerously close, so you must always use a password when approached at night, even if you think you recognize somebody. During the day, you need only use the password if you are not sure of someone's identity.

A password is always in two parts. For example, you challenge 'Plum', and you then expect an answer or countersign – say 'Pie'. If you are operating with NATO forces, on the other hand, the use of the phonetic alphabet is the agreed procedure. So if you challenge 'November', you might expect the answer or countersign 'Tango'. Passwords are changed daily at 1200 hours.

In real life you wouldn't, and shouldn't ever, use a password as obvious as 'plum' and 'pie' – for instance you might answer 'plum' with 'road'. A more secure system is to use pairs of letters, for example 'ARPN'. The challenge is 'Alpha romeo', and the answer 'Papa november'. Once again don't use four-letter

# THE GROUND SENTRY

A ground sentry must know:

1. The location of his post, neighbouring posts and his own back-up or covering sentry.
2. The time he will be relieved and by whom.
3. How he will be relieved – e.g. whether or not he has to fetch his replacement.
4. State of enemy forces.
5. Arcs of observation and fire.
6. What to do on hearing or seeing suspicious activity.
7. How to alert the rest of his section.
8. Correct procedure for challenging.
9. Orders for opening fire.
10. Concealment.
11. When friendly patrols will be moving in or out of the position.
12. Location of mines, trip flares, etc.
13. Password or passnumber.

*Ground sentries must be very carefully briefed and monitored to check they have understood the information in their orders. Ideally they should have at least two methods of alerting the section.*

# AIR SENTRY

An air sentry must know:

1 The location of his post.
2 The length of his stag, and the time and method of relief.
3 The air situation: who has air superiority.
4 Arc of observation: 6400 mils if possible.
5 Types of hostile aircraft to be expected.
6 Method of raising the alarm.
7 Orders for opening fire.
8 Concealment from the air.

**Threat assessment**
The Soviet special forces and 'fifth columnists' will probably not wait for war to be declared to attack their targets. How sentries are deployed and used depends on an accurate assessment of the range of threats that need to be countered.

**Sentry changeover**
Sentry positions can be easily compromised by sloppy changeover procedure. Tactical sentry positions should only be approached along the predesignated track plan, which should ideally be a covered approach. The only briefing that should go on actually in the sentry position should be confirmation of arcs of observation and fire; the rest of the brief should be given in safe area.

**Surveillance devices**
Sentries should be equipped with binoculars and night vision devices. Passive night vision goggles are tiring to use and ruin your unaided night vision, so only one sentry in a pair should use them. The other scans using the Mark One Eyeball. Swap roles every 20 minutes or so.

**Two by two**
Sentries should always be deployed in twos for adequate protection.

**Radios and field telephones**
Radios are noisy and can signal a tactical sentry position to the enemy before the sentry can see them. Field telephones are less noisy but you must work out a plan to avoid giving up the sentry as the dialtone may be overheard.

**Weapons**
Tactical sentries are usually equipped with automatic weapons, eg the GPMG or the LSW. Sentries would also be able to fire the Claymores if you had any out. They should also have an ample supply of grenades and Schermulys or perhaps the 51-mm mortar.

**Stand off attack**
Sentries should not be limited to the confines of an installation they are protecting. Frequent patrols should be used to check for mortar baseplates or enemy equipped with laser target markers beyond the perimeter.

words or combinations that can easily be guessed.

Another system uses a single-number password. This might mean the passnumber is seven. The sentry then challenges 'Three', requiring the answer 'Four' (i.e, three plus four equals seven). But keep the numbers

# Combat Skills

## CHALLENGE PROCEDURE FOR SENTRIES

**SENTRY:**
1. "HALT! WHO IS (or GOES) THERE?"

   **Person or group challenged:**
   Halts and gives any reply which indicates the person or group is authorised to pass, e.g. "FRIEND", "ALLY", "CORPORAL OF THE GUARD", etc

2. "ADVANCE (ONE) AND BE RECOGNISED"

   One person (e.g. group leader) advances without replying

3. "HALT" (When the unknown person has approached sufficiently for sentry to recognise him or to give challenge)

   Person halts until recognised by sentry

4. Challenge (if any) is given in a low tone

   Reply or countersign is given in a low tone

5. "ADVANCE ANOTHER ONE (or REMAINDER) AND BE RECOGNISED". (Sentry calls forward remainder one by one or as a group, as the situation or his orders demand)

   Second unknown (or remainder of group) advances at order of sentry to be recognised. Group leader, or person designated by leader must remain with sentry to assist in identifying remainder

*Advance the first man, keeping him in your sights and halt him close enough to see him. Be suspicious of anyone who advances towards you with his weapon at the ready.*

*The patrol commander or the scout you have just identified should then join you and count the patrol members in. Watch the enemy in case they have tagged a couple of their own blokes on the end of the patrol.*

*The challenge procedure is all a question of timing. You must challenge anyone approaching your position when he is not close enough to rush you or so far away that you could miss him if he runs away.*

*When entering your own position after a long patrol, fight the natural tendency to switch off. Mistakes at this stage cost lives in the Falklands war.*

Do this at a range that will let the section kill any enemy who try to run away, but not so close that the enemy could rush you before you have a chance to do anything about it. If the order to halt is not obeyed, repeat it and, if it is still not obeyed, you have no choice but to follow the orders for opening fire.

### Stick to the rules

This procedure must be followed exactly. Otherwise, fatal mistakes can happen. Common mistakes are to halt approaching figures either too far away — in which case, if they are enemy, they are given the opportunity to escape — or too close, which could allow an enemy to rush you and overpower you. Another serious error, easy when the adrenalin is high, is to forget to alert your section commander by tugging on your communication cord (or whatever other signal you have devised) when you first see a figure or figures approaching your position.

### Lying doggo

However dark the night, you will have the advantage of lying on the ground and being stationary. You will therefore see or hear (or both) the enemy long before he is aware of your presence, particularly if you have a night vision device. By the time he is dangerously close, you should have the firepower of the remainder of your section backing you up.

### Night and day

When you are tired, sleep is at a premium, and everyone is very conscious of their 'ration', so sentry watches must be carefully and evenly divided. Sentries always work in pairs at night. Watches can be as short as half an hour but should not exceed two hours. You should use the shorter watch when you are working in extreme climatic conditions. But you must also ensure that reliefs of sentries happen properly, otherwise a whole sentry roster can break down during the night if someone falls asleep on sentry duty. This happens even in the best-trained armies.

Stagger reliefs of tactical sentries to ensure that one is always fresher than the other. This method also ensures that the sight of at least one sentry is always well converted to night vision and night conditions. He should then not be alarmed by the night calls of various animals or the shape of trees and bushes that could otherwise be mistaken for the shape of a man.

By day there should not be too

simple and don't expect people to do complicated mental arithmetic. If the passnumber is 43, the sentry might challenge '17', and then blow somebody's head off just for getting his sums wrong.

Asking for the password is only one part of the challenging procedure — which you must always follow

exactly. If you fail to use the standard procedure you could confuse friendly returning patrols and inflict casualties on your own troops. If any unexpected person or group approaches your position, alert the section commander. If he thinks it necessary, he will 'stand to' the section. But it's your job to do the actual challenging.

much of a problem. When you are out of immediate contact with the enemy, one ground and one chemical/air sentry for a platoon is normally sufficient. If there is no chemical threat, one tactical/air sentry could suffice. By night, two tactical and one chemical/air sentries are required per platoon. If you are in close contact with the enemy, post one tactical sentry for each section and one chemical/air sentry for the platoon by day, and double the number of tactical sentries by night.

## Supervision system

All this is complicated to set up and to maintain. It will fail unless supervised, however well-intentioned and trained individual sentries are, so you must set up a system of supervision. There are various methods: the platoon commander and platoon sergeant can split responsibility for the night, or section commanders can contribute towards watchkeeping duties at platoon HQ. At section level, the section commander and 2IC can split the night, or sentries post themselves but report to the section 2IC when they are about to wake the relieving sentry. Whatever method you use, remember that supervision is necessary.

At night, one of the two sentries must always man one of the section LSWs fitted with an IWS. This provides immediate and concentrated fire power which will alert the other members of the section to go to their alarm positions.

## Specialists at watching

The jobs of chemical and air sentries will normally be combined. The task of an air sentry is quite simple: he warns his section or platoon of an impending air attack on them. It is not his job to engage aircraft attacking other targets. That will be the job of local air defence weapon systems, and possibly of his platoon or section automatic weapons. An air sentry must be good at aircraft recognition so that he can distinguish between friendlies and hostiles: even so, the first indication you might get that an aircraft is hostile is cannon shells landing around you or bombs being tossed in your direction. Before engaging the attacker, however, always remember the best protection is concealment – so don't compromise your position unnecessarily.

Chemical sentries are sited downwind of a platoon and are equipped with detection paper that will indicate the presence of a blister agent, as well

*Above: US Army Rangers practise sentry take-down techniques. Do not forget that you as a sentry are a vital source of immediate battlefield intelligence to the enemy. They may be after you.*

*Left: You should observe your arc, looking over your sights in a good fire position so you don't attract attention by moving. Who gets the first round off is always important.*

*This sentry has made no real effort to camouflage himself or his position. The rifle is not in the shoulder and he would not be able to use the field telephone if he came under fire.*

*A moment's lapse of concentration and you could miss that glimpse of the enemy recce. This sort of thing will result in you being charged in war. It can also get you killed.*

as a machine called NAIAD (Nerve Agent Immobilized Enzyme Alarm and Detector), which will detect nerve agents. Chemical agents can be delivered by means of artillery shells, rockets or aircraft spray. A sentry must look out for all three, and then trust his detector paper or NAIAD. He will already be wearing his protective equipment, but must warn the platoon – either by radio, or by banging two metal objects such as mess tins to-

gether and shouting 'Gas, Gas, Gas.' If he is quick, this will give his comrades time to put their gas masks on and survive the attack.

Sentry duties are crucially important. They may be a bore, particularly when you are tired and you'd rather be in your warm sleeping bag. But you would never be forgiven – or forgive yourself – if you failed in your duty and were responsible for your comrades' deaths.

# Combat Report
## Zanzibar:
## Quelling the Riots Part 1

**A Major with the King's African Rifles in Kenya recalls the time he moved his men into Zanzibar in order to quell the violent disturbances that had broken out there.**

The little Arab girl had been very lovely. Now, the savage slash of a panga had cleaved across her right eye, and the side of her face. She would live, but was horribly scarred for the rest of her life. The child lay in a nurse's arms, and her remaining good eye looked out tearfully at the cruel world beyond.

This was on Zanzibar, the beautiful island lying twenty two miles off the coast of East Africa in the year 1961. The island, roughly the size of Hampshire, has had a turbulent history, and was mentioned in records as long ago as 60 AD. It became the centre of the East African slave trade, and remained so until 1879.

Now, in 1961, an election was being held, and as the island's population of Africans, Arabs and Indians with a sprinkling of other races, had lived peaceably together for many years, the official view was that there would be no disturbances.

At that time I was serving as a Major with 5th Battalion, The King's African Rifles, at Nakuru in Kenya, which lies in the glorious Rift Valley about 100 miles from the capital, Nairobi. We were the standby battalion for the whole of East Africa at that time, and were frequently sent off to deal with Mau Mau remnants, poachers, or inter tribal skirmishes. Our African soldiers were long serving, tough professionals. The Battalion were all in barracks, and no operations appeared to be pending, which was just fine by the Officers because on 3 June there was to be a Regimental wedding. One of our Captains was marrying an air hostess, and the party promised to be a good one.

### Violent disturbances

Then on 1 June, we received the order that one company was to stand by in view of the general election in Zanzibar. However the order was not taken very seriously, apart from normal preparation of kit, because two Kenya Police General Service Units (GSU) had already gone to Zanzibar. These were very tough cookies by any standard, they carried a lot of weaponry and stood no nonsense from anyone. There would have to be spectacular trouble if the two GSUs could not handle it. So we focused our attention on more important things, like the Regimental wedding!

However on 2 June we were rudely shaken out of our complacency when reports began to come in concerning violent disturbances in Zanzibar. The news grew worse and worse, with information about savage rioting and rising casualties. Both the Police General Service Units were in action, and were obviously battling hard to keep some measure of control.

Then the order came that our standby company, together with Battalion Tactical Headquarters, were to move to the island, and they were to be followed immediately by a further rifle company and our Reconnaissance Platoon. Moves were to start at 0500 hrs the following morning from RAF Station, Eastleigh, Nairobi, 100 miles away.

I personally was to act as Second in Command of the Battalion for this operation, and I was to move with the second company sometime on the morning of 3 June. We spent the whole night organising, packing and weighing our equipment for the airlift. By mid morning the following day I was at the RAF Station, helping to supervise the loading of soldiers, vehicles and stores on to the giant Beverley aircraft for our flight to Zanzibar. Tactical Headquarters and the first company had already left a few hours earlier, and were by that time probably in action, as flying time to the island was about two and half hours. The news was still grim from Zanzibar, and up to that time the official number of known dead was eighteen, with hundreds injured. The General Service Units had done a magnificent job, but had been in action continuously for about 48 hours without relief and were now on the point of exhaustion. So it was vital that we got our soldiers on the ground and operating as soon as possible. Violence still continued.

My flight was uneventful, and we soon came smoothly down onto the runway of Zanzibar airport. The buildings were of a unique design, a sort of Moorish character to them. The place seemed almost deserted, apart from a line of Public Works Department lorries awaiting us.

The original drivers had all fled in terror, and the present drivers were European businessmen, who had volunteered for this quite dangerous duty. The driver of the lorry I travelled in was a bank manager, for example.

We motored through streets full of rubble and debris. Dead bodies were still being recovered, and many wounded were being located and given attention. The smoke of burning, looted buildings drifted across this sad scene.

Our Tactical Headquarters was located in an abandoned school in the city, and I discovered that 'B' Company was already in action against rioters. 'A' Company, which I had travelled with, plus the Reconnaissance Platoon, dumped their heavy kit, quickly received orders and then they too went off on operations.

Mobs were still battling in various places, and the Africans (in the majority) were causing dreadful wounds on the Arabs and Indians with their pangas, the long bladed African bush knives.

**Above: An RAF Beverley transport aircraft taking off from Kenya in order to carry a detachment of the King's African Rifles to Zanzibar.**

**Below: When we arrived the streets were blocked with rubble and burned-out vehicles. Mobs were fighting it out in several places.**

# Combat Skills
# TAKING PRISONERS

*At the point of capture you must have at least one man with a clear shot at the prisoner, safety catch off, until you are sure you have got rid of all his weapons. When fighting through an enemy position, remember that they are unlikely to surrender all at the same time. Get the enemy to come to you, and do not get up out of cover to accept the surrender.*

**Prisoners in war can arrive in battalions or as single men or women who have been flushed out of a position after a hard fight, and may be gravely wounded.** If they qualify for Prisoner of War status, whatever way they arrive, the rules are the same. You are required to treat them in a humane manner and they are required only to give their name, rank, number and date of birth.

You are required to provide medical care for prisoners who are sick or wounded. Although you may search prisoners for weapons and items of intelligence value, they should be allowed to retain their personal possessions. Money and valuables may only be removed for safe keeping on the order of an officer. During the course of questioning a prisoner, you may not use torture or threats. You can use PoWs to do work which is not related to the war effort — for example, carrying your wounded to the rear.

A PoW is still the enemy and represents a source of intelligence and possible threat to security behind your lines. When he surrenders, the enemy soldier experiences a defineable psychological state called the 'shock of capture'. In this state he is often passive and co-operative. As the shock wears off he begins to become alert and to look at ways of resisting his captors. You should aim to keep the

*The lone enemy soldier with an automatic weapon can do a good deal of damage, so isolate the prisoner from any outside interference and then subdue him as quickly as possible. The faster you get rid of all the means at his disposal to shoot you or blow you up, the better.*

# PRISONER HANDLING DRILL

**2** Split into pairs and do a quick but thoroug[h] weapon search. Use the same technique us[ed] for searching bodies, covered by your budd[y]. You are looking for grenades, pistols and kn[ives]. You must leave him with his helmet and NB[C] suit as you are in a forward area. His person[al] belongings may be of use during questionin[g]. Do not talk to the prisoners other than to pa[ss] on commands, and do not allow them to tal[k to] each other. Give any first aid necessary, an[d] water. Do not give food or cigarettes or oth[er] comforts at this stage.

**1** At the point of capture you must encourage the enemy to surrender while minimising your own vulnerability. The enemy should come to you. Look through the sights of your weapon with the safety off, ready to fire a round with no chance of missing. If there is a large group of prisoners they should be encouraged to dump their weapons, covered by GPMG and halted at a suitable distance from your position so there is no chance of them overrunning you. All this may be a little difficult on the modern battlefield. If you have wounded an enemy, you may have to go and get him: this should be done in covered bounds as in fire-and-manoeuvre.

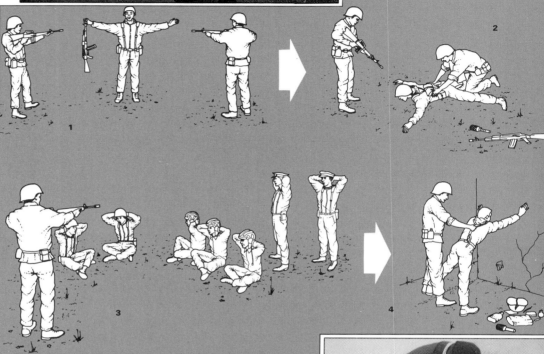

**3** Segregate the prisoners by rank into officers, NCOs and private soldiers. It is also a good idea to separate any special forces such as airborne troops from the rest, as they will have to be more closely guarded. You can usually employ any able-bodied POWs to look after and carry back the wounded, both theirs and yours. Once you get back to platoon HQ, the platoon sergeant will take charge and will usually have an escort party to take the prisoners back to company HQ. If you are short of escorts, cuff-lock the prisoner's hands behind their backs.

**4** The prisoners will be escorted back with the wounded, via the company HQ and the company aid post, back to battalion where there is both the prisoner cage and the regimental aid post. Before putting them in the cage, search each prisoner thoroughly and place all the contents of his kit in a bag tied to his back. Most of his combat kit, such as helmet and webbing, should be taken off him at this stage.

shock of capture going as long as possible down the evacuation chain to the rear. A PoW's best opportunity for escape is when he is still near the forward line of troops; as he moves deeper into (to him) enemy-controlled territory, these chances diminish.

The first thing to do with a PoW is to disarm and search him. Look for weapons: everything from small arms to knives and any tools that may assist escape. All documents, except individual identification papers, should also be taken and tagged to identify their owner. The PoW will have been given a number for handling purposes and this will also be attached to his possessions and documents.

If a PoW is separated from his possessions, a tactical questioner will have less to work on when he interrogates him. Thus a man who sticks to the 'Big Four' — name, rank, number and date of birth — but who has the specialist equipment, documents and details of where and when he was captured will be easier to break down than a totally anonymous PoW. During the search phase a Capture Card should be attached to the PoW. This will include the time and place of capture and any special circumstances. All of this information helps the questioner further down the line.

## Searching a prisoner

Searching can range from the emptying of ammunition pouches and pockets through to a strip search in which clothing is examined in detail. However, do not deprive a PoW of clothing that may protect him from the elements or from hazards of artillery or NBC attack. He can keep his helmet and NBC suit while the danger still exists.

While searching, check the small of the back, which is a good place to conceal items like knives or hand guns, and squeeze pockets. Do not pat them, since this will not reveal papers or flat objects.

Your search must be systematic: start with the inside of his helmet, then examine his hair, collar, combat jacket, shirt, armpits and small of the back. When searching clothing, roll the material between your finger tips to see if anything has been sewn in. Watch the prisoner while you search his kit: a changing facial expression may tell you that you are approaching

**5** All prisoners should be interrogated for information of immediate intelligence value as quickly as possible, while the shock of capture is still in operation: this could be carried out by Intelligence Corps personnel involved in gathering battlefield intelligence. They will assess the importance and intelligence value of each prisoner, and their success depends largely on how well you have handled the prisoners. Each prisoner will be labelled and moved back to the brigade intelligence cell for further questioning.

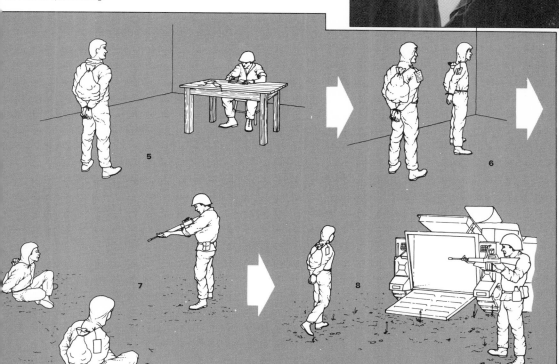

**6** After the initial debrief the prisoners should be moved back from the forward area as quickly as possible. The further back they go, the less likely they are to escape. They should now be without their webbing, which further decreases their ability to make a run for it. The silence rule should still be enforced, and fair but firm treatment should be used. Give them food and water, but again no comforts such as cigarettes.

**8** Be especially careful when moving the prisoners back by vehicle. The prisoners should be cuff-locked and hooded and a thorough search made of the vehicle afterwards to make sure they have not attempted to hide any documents in the vehicle. Do not gag a prisoner: he could choke on the gag. If you have the means, every item of the prisoner's kit, including his weapon and a full write-up of how and where he was captured, should accompany him.

**7** Obviously the level of attention you can give to your prisoners depends on how many POWs you have and how many men you can spare to guard them. If you have the resources, prisoners should be bound and hooded and preferably guarded on a one-to-one basis. When you stop, always sit them down cross-legged and far enough apart to prevent them passing things between them.

*A North Vietnamese regular sits blindfolded and handcuffed in the back of a jeep waiting to be moved to a specialist interrogation centre in the Central Highlands of South Vietnam.*

something vital – or even that you have missed something.

If the prisoner is carrying a radio, check what frequency it is working on and report this as soon as possible. Where there's a radio there'll be some signal instructions, so find them quickly. In a strip search, don't forget the groin area, which is a favourite hiding place for all sorts of items. You'd be amazed at what you can find taped behind someone's testicles during escape and evasion exercises. Note that female prisoners can only be strip searched by WRAC personnel.

The traditional search position favoured in the best American police films is a perfectly effective one. The PoW rests his extended arms against a wall or tree, and by a careful prod with his feet the searcher pushes the PoW's feet far enough apart and away from the wall so that the PoW's arms are taking the weight. As he searches, the soldier is covered by a companion who moves so that the PoW always stays in his sights. If the searcher is alone, he can use a hand gun. The position that the PoW is standing in allows the searcher to kick his feet away and so drop him on the ground if the PoW makes any attempt to resist the search or to escape.

Other positions can put the PoW prone on the ground or with his legs crossed and hands on his head with fingers interlocked. Keeping the hands on the head or back of the neck is less tiring than merely putting them in the air, and has the advantage that it takes a few seconds longer for the PoW to disentangle his fingers and lower his arms if he plans to make an attack or to escape. Prone on the

# POW HANDLING TRAINING

**Above:** POW handling does not come naturally – you have to train for it just like everything else. You must learn the safest way to handle a prisoner who could be trained to a very high standard in unarmed combat. This is the right way to do it: if the prisoner makes a move, you are not going to miss.

**Below:** The spreadeagle position is by far the best for the initial weapons search. Place one foot between the prisoner's legs ready for use in case of trouble. The cover here is practically useless: he has the stock folded down and is not ready to fire a shot, and the weapon is not even pointing at the prisoner. If you have to act, all you should have to do is take up the last pressure on the trigger.

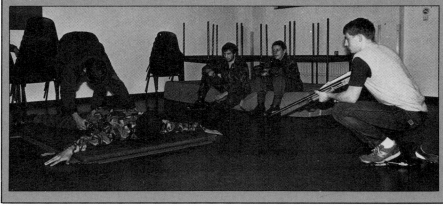

ground is also a difficult position from which to move fast, but 'wall propping' or hands in the air is still the best position for searching. After a search is over the PoW can be ordered into a crossed-leg position while searchers move on to another prisoner.

## Segregate

Split groups down into officers, NCOs, junior ranks, deserters, civilians, females and political indoctrination personnel. This prevents leaders from imposing order and escape plans as well as making the other PoWs more security-conscious. It also assists tactical questioners in identifying the worthwhile PoWs to interrogate.

If you have a mass of PoWs, one way of identifying the leaders is to look for rank badges. If these have been removed, give the group an order and see if they look to a particular PoW for guidance about whether they should obey the order. Even the reactions of PoWs to an order will be a guide — soldiers will be quicker and more willing to react than officers or NCOs. The senior ranks may also keep themselves separate from the soldiers even if they are all in one group. While they are being moved to the rear, make sure that they stay separated into groups.

## Silence

Do not allow PoWs to talk. This prevents them from discussing escape or cautioning each other on security. Silence and an absolutely neutral 'firm but fair' approach will sustain

*When escorting a prisoner, always walk behind him and far enough away so that he cannot make a grab for your rifle. Prisoners should always be escorted with bayonets fitted so you have a choice of weapon. There is no point trussing up a co-operative prisoner like a chicken and blindfolding him if you then have to walk miles from point of capture.*

# THE LAMP POST LOCK

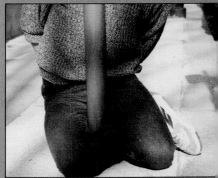

If you have to deal with a number of prisoners in a built-up area, you can secure them to the lamp posts as shown above. It takes two men to put the prisoner in this position: one to fold the legs and one to pick him up. The average man cannot get out of this position without help, even with his hands free. Traffic signs are too thin and you will need to cuff the prisoner too.

You can quickly reduce the mobility of the prisoner by tying a short length of cord between his legs or simply by removing his boots. Whenever you stop, blindfold and segregate the prisoners.

Below: Koreans question a couple of potential Viet Cong just extracted from the huge bunker behind them. The Koreans had a grim reputation for being fairly uncompromising when dealing with VC prisoners. Remember, if the enemy know you are not in the habit of taking prisoners they are not going to give up, and you will take more casualties.

the shock of capture. If you are aggressive in your PoW handling this can be damaging on two counts: it may so terrify the man that he will say anything to stop being bullied — and agree to any idea that is suggested. This does not produce military intelligence, and can produce false confessions.

Also, bullying or brutality can harden a PoW. He may look at his captors and decide that silence is the only form of resistance that he can adopt in the face of this illegal behaviour.

## Speed

Move PoWs to the rear as fast as possible, away from the area they are familiar with and to skilled questioners who will want to extract intelligence that is hours, not days, old.

## Safeguard

Guarding prisoners can be for their own good as well as to prevent them from escaping: hostile civilians as well as troops in the rear areas can be a problem.

If you fraternise with your prisoners this can sustain or raise morale, and the silent but firm and fair approach will convince a PoW that he is in the hands of professional troops.

Rioters in Aden await interrogation in a stress position watched over by members of the Parachute Regiment. The Sten gun is not the way to deal with minor infringements of the rules such as talking: walking tall and carrying a big stick is far more appropriate.

# Combat Report
## Zanzibar:
## Quelling the Riots Part 2

**Continued involvement of the King's African Rifles in Zanzibar before it became independent.**

I was given permission to take out a patrol to familiarise myself with the situation, so getting a Land Rover and driver and arranging our Provost Sergeant and a couple of his men as escort, I went into the city. Casualties were still streaming into the main hospital and, as we paused there, we saw the pathetic sight of the disfigured Arab girl described above. Other wounded were carried in on stretchers or assisted there by relatives or friends. The violence had been quite indiscriminate and we saw old men and women and several other young children all brutally chopped about their heads and bodies.

We continued the patrol and reached a spot where a violent mob had only recently been dispersed. The surrounding area, with wreckage and smoke blackened buildings gave evidence of this. Standing at a road junction was a Kenya Police Land Rover, and sitting wearily in it (with his signaller and escort of course) was the Commander of the General Service Units. He was a splendid Irishman, who had commanded his tough men brilliantly during the first hectic two days. I chatted to him for a short while and what he told me made me realise that had such prompt action by Security Forces not been taken, a quite awesome situation would have arisen. Now, with the arrival of 5 KAR, the GSUs were being relieved to get a well earned rest for at least one day.

We then enforced a curfew, and the soldiers of 5 KAR continued to deal firmly with any rioters or looters that they came across. Nevertheless, although in Zanzibar City the situation was slowly coming under control, dead bodies and wounded continued to be discovered. The night of 3-4 June passed reasonably peaceably, but then on the morning of 4 June, reports of trouble began to come in from rural areas which previously had been quiet. About this time I took my little patrol out again, and just outside the city, after a brief scuffle, we arrested a man armed with the most fearsome looking sort of bill hook.

The next threat of trouble came via reports from the neighbouring island of Pemba. There, the District Commissioner sent messages saying he was sure violence was about to break out, and that the few policemen on the island would be quickly overwhelmed. It was therefore decided I would fly to Pemba in a civilian light aircraft of the Zanzibar Government. Apart from the fact that all services at Zanzibar airport had ceased, and the place was deserted, and that my civilian pilot had no map, the journey across the seas was uneventful.

I spent a number of hours with the District Commissioner and he was firmly convinced that if troops were not sent to Pemba there would be a bloodbath there. I therefore recommended that one Infantry company be sent. By this time even more reinforcements were on the way to Zanzibar, our own 'C' Company from Kenya plus two companies from 6 KAR in Tanganyika. One

of the 6 KAR sub units went to Pemba, and things there remained quiet as a result.

As our soldiers moved out of the city into the countryside on Zanzibar they discovered several sites of massacres, where whole families had been cut to pieces or burnt to death in their house. But now the military and police were very much on top of the situation, many troublemakers had been arrested and peace of a sort was returning to the island. By 10 June the situation was completely under control, and by that time there were approximately one hundred dead, many hundreds wounded (a great many of whom were never officially reported) and the Security Forces had made about 1,500 arrests. We had killed and wounded several gangsters when bringing the trouble under control.

So the soldiers of the KAR were eventually returned to their bases, having been relieved by a British Unit who remained as a garrison. A special para military unit of the Zanzibar Police was trained to be ready by the time of their Independence in 1963.

Sadly, all that had been achieved was in vain. Independence came as planned in 1963, but then in January 1964 gangs from the mainland landed on Zanzibar one night. They were heavily armed with automatic weapons and were led by an ex-Mau Mau terrorist trained in Cuba. The new para military force were mostly slaughtered in their beds. Then, the murder, rape and pillage on the island made our riots of 1961 look like a children's tea party. There were no soldiers of the King's African Rifles to rescue to victims this time.

No official figures were ever given, but the dead were estimated as about eight thousand. The dazed population then found themselves controlled by a revolutionary government. But of course that is another story.

**Above: Venturing into the lush undergrowth in search of the surviving rebels. This officer carries a Sten Mk 5 sub-machine gun.**

**Left: An RAF Beverley flies from Tanganyika bringing two companies of 6 KAR to support the pacification operation in Zanzibar.**

# TACTICAL QUESTIONING

**The aim of tactical questioning is to gain intelligence of immediate value to the capturing unit.** This short-term information is in contrast to long-term intelligence. Long-term information about brigade, divisional or corps level operations will only be of use at higher levels of your command. It will also only be held by senior enemy officers, and if you capture them they should be moved away from the front line as fast as possible to trained interrogators.

## Not an interrogation

It is important to understand the distinction between questioning and interrogation. Interrogation is a skill which is acquired after special training. It is normally practised in a secure environment where the interrogator has time to talk with the prisoner. There may also be scope for the use of sensory deprivation techniques involving 'white noise', wall standing and loose-fitting clothing. These all combine to give the prisoner a sense of isolation and make him more vulnerable when he is confronted by his interrogator. He will in effect 'want' to talk because he will feel a desire to communicate with another person and will see the interrogation periods as a break from the monotony of sensory deprivation.

In the front line you will be able only to *question* a prisoner. Quiz him about short-term intelligence matters. Even here, questioning should be

*An aggressor force prisoner is closely questioned by an intelligence corps officer prior to being moved to the POW cage. Trained questioners should work as far forward as possible to take full advantage of the shock of capture.*

done by qualified personnel. In training, this can be very important. A unit cannot 'set up' an exercise without clearance at a high level and without the participants being briefed on their role, medical assistance being available and tight control by directing staff. In conditions of stress and fatigue men can suffer temporary or even permanent psychological damage. It is a waste of a soldier's potential if he becomes a psychological casualty in training and can be just as damaging as external physical injury.

In war, it is also important to pass a prisoner on to trained and experienced questioners. Good prisoner handling keeps the prisoner in a vulnerable state ready for his questioner. A tactical questioner should speak the language of the man he is talking to. During the Falklands campaign, the MoD searched for Spanish linguists and were lucky to build up a small pool. A small map of the Falklands was printed with the Argentine names for towns and features marked in. Armed with this, the questioner could ask where a soldier had been based and other tactical details.

The initial search reveals information about the prisoner. In the Falklands, many Argentine soldiers carried letters – these had not only names and ranks, but regimental and company details. During the search, any escape equipment will be removed and if personal items are removed they should be tagged and signed for.

## Trick him into talking

Sometimes seeing his belongings being handled will loosen a prisoner's tongue if he has stuck to 'the big four'. The Geneva Convention states that upon capture a soldier is obliged to give only his name, rank, date of birth and service number. In war these would be forwarded to a neutral power and then back to the soldier's home country. He would then be listed as a PoW and not missing.

The aim of the questioner is to trick

# TACTICAL QUESTIONING

*Before you start the questioning process you must know all you can about the subject – not just his name, rank and unit, but what part of the Soviet Union he comes from, what type of unit he commands and what tactics are commonly used, and where his unit was last deployed. With a sound base you can then ask the right questions. Remember that most battlefield intelligence is only of use if it can be extracted and acted upon within 24 hours.*

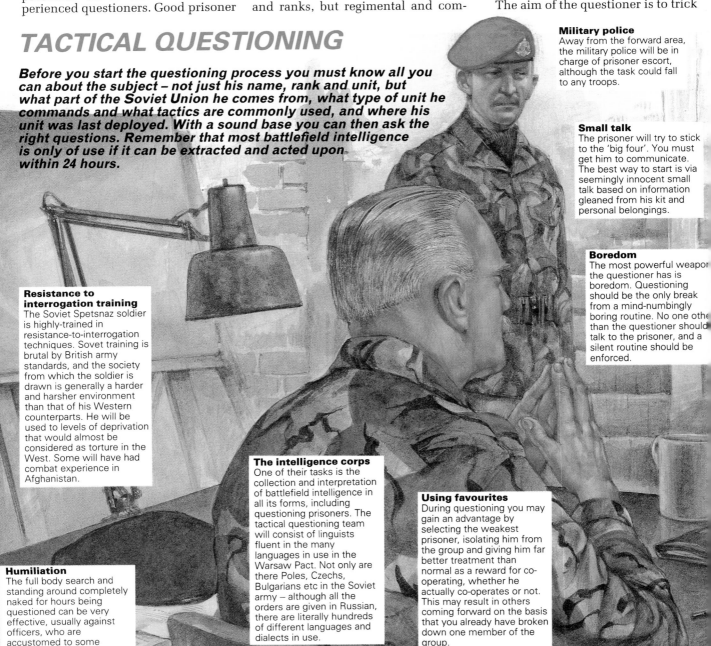

**Military police**
Away from the forward area, the military police will be in charge of prisoner escort, although the task could fall to any troops.

**Small talk**
The prisoner will try to stick to the 'big four'. You must get him to communicate. The best way to start is via seemingly innocent small talk based on information gleaned from his kit and personal belongings.

**Boredom**
The most powerful weapon the questioner has is boredom. Questioning should be the only break from a mind-numbingly boring routine. No one other than the questioner should talk to the prisoner, and a silent routine should be enforced.

**Resistance to interrogation training**
The Soviet Spetsnaz soldier is highly-trained in resistance-to-interrogation techniques. Sovet training is brutal by British army standards, and the society from which the soldier is drawn is generally a harder and harsher environment than that of his Western counterparts. He will be used to levels of deprivation that would almost be considered as torture in the West. Some will have had combat experience in Afghanistan.

**The intelligence corps**
One of their tasks is the collection and interpretation of battlefield intelligence in all its forms, including questioning prisoners. The tactical questioning team will consist of linguists fluent in the many languages in use in the Warsaw Pact. Not only are there Poles, Czechs, Bulgarians etc in the Soviet army – although all the orders are given in Russian, there are literally hundreds of different languages and dialects in use.

**Using favourites**
During questioning you may gain an advantage by selecting the weakest prisoner, isolating him from the group and giving him far better treatment than normal as a reward for co-operating, whether he actually co-operates or not. This may result in others coming forward on the basis that you already have broken down one member of the group.

**Humiliation**
The full body search and standing around completely naked for hours being questioned can be very effective, usually against officers, who are accustomed to some respect. This may have limited effect on a hardened Soviet soldier.

or bully the prisoner into talking. Initially this can be something quite simple like answering a non-military question. If the prisoner begins to relax and talk, the questioner will press on. If *you* are a prisoner, remember that talking will not help you by ingratiating you with your captors. They will see you not as being helpful and pleasant, but weak and thus someone who should be pushed harder. A PoW's best ploy is to convince the questioner that he is a simple soldier who knows very little.

As a questioner, you want 'value for money'. The radio operator, company commander, company-sergeant-major, ideally the colonel, are the

*During internal security operations questioning is the province of the police. Many tactical questioning techniques may render any information or evidence inadmissible in court as a forced confession.*

### utral background
e room chosen for
rying out questioning
uld be free of any
ential distractions, e.g.
icle movement outside.
re should be no posters
other points of interest in
room: it must be as
tral as possible.

### ation
e of any value, prisoners
t not be allowed to
municate in any way.
munication will allow
 to impose their own
plinary code and cook
ories between them.
 prisoner must believe
he is on his own.

### Playing the innocent
The soft approach is to let the prisoner think he is dealing with a fool and that he has the upper hand. This method builds reliable intelligence slowly.

### Sensory deprivation
These techniques have to be used very carefully in training as they can be extremely damaging if mismanaged. Such methods rely on removing as many external stimuli as possible. This includes equipping the prisoner with loose-fitting clothes, taking away his watch and keeping him in complete silence with electric lighting so that there is no way he can judge the passage of time.

### Altering the perception of reality
Sensory deprivation, isolation and boredom, coupled with the shock of capture and fatigue, will make it difficult for the prisoner to differentiate fact from fiction. Soldiers undergoing resistance-to-interrogation training have often become completely convinced that they are at war or that their captors genuinely believe that they are terrorists. It may be possible to convince the prisoner that the war is over or that the whole thing was a training exercise.

### Uniform
You must know the value of your prisoners. This means learning the rank systems of the Warsaw Pact and being able to identify the different units. The sky-blue beret of the Soviet airborne division is also worn by army Spetsnaz.

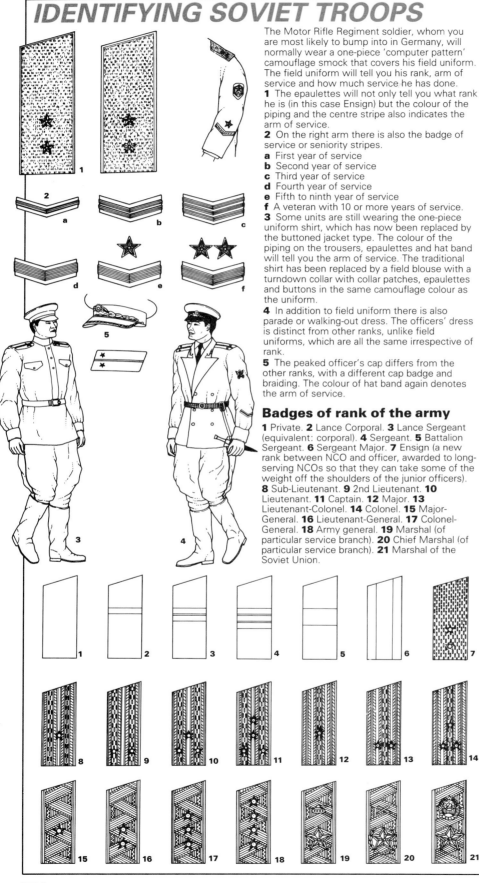

# IDENTIFYING SOVIET TROOPS

The Motor Rifle Regiment soldier, whom you are most likely to bump into in Germany, will normally wear a one-piece 'computer pattern' camouflage smock that covers his field uniform. The field uniform will tell you his rank, arm of service and how much service he has done.

**1** The epaulettes will not only tell you what rank he is (in this case Ensign) but the colour of the piping and the centre stripe also indicates the arm of service.

**2** On the right arm there is also the badge of service or seniority stripes.

**a** First year of service
**b** Second year of service
**c** Third year of service
**d** Fourth year of service
**e** Fifth to ninth year of service
**f** A veteran with 10 or more years of service.

**3** Some units are still wearing the one-piece uniform shirt, which has now been replaced by the buttoned jacket type. The colour of the piping on the trousers, epaulettes and hat band will tell you the arm of service. The traditional shirt has been replaced by a field blouse with a turndown collar with collar patches, epaulettes and buttons in the same camouflage colour as the uniform.

**4** In addition to field uniform there is also parade or walking-out dress. The officers' dress is distinct from other ranks, unlike field uniforms, which are all the same irrespective of rank.

**5** The peaked officer's cap differs from the other ranks, with a different cap badge and braiding. The colour of hat band again denotes the arm of service.

## Badges of rank of the army

**1** Private. **2** Lance Corporal. **3** Lance Sergeant (equivalent: corporal). **4** Sergeant. **5** Battalion Sergeant. **6** Sergeant Major. **7** Ensign (a new rank between NCO and officer, awarded to long-serving NCOs so that they can take some of the weight off the shoulders of the junior officers). **8** Sub-Lieutenant. **9** 2nd Lieutenant. **10** Lieutenant. **11** Captain. **12** Major. **13** Lieutenant-Colonel. **14** Colonel. **15** Major-General. **16** Lieutenant-General. **17** Colonel-General. **18** Army general. **19** Marshal (of particular service branch). **20** Chief Marshal (of particular service branch). **21** Marshal of the Soviet Union.

people to talk to. Find them among the prisoners – clearly insignia will be a guide, but also age and behaviour will show who is in command.

As you attempt to wear down, trick, or bully the prisoner, start with a neutral tone asking 'the big four'. This allows you the freedom to switch to other techniques. One Spanish-speaking British officer talked informally to the crew of the submarine *Santa Fe* in South Georgia; his apparently naive manner and innocent chatter concealed a steady build-up of information.

## Catch him out

The questioner must have a clear idea about what he wants from the prisoner. It may be a very simple piece of information. A very skilled German questioner in World War II described how he would find out details of dog-fighting tactics from captured USAF Mustang pilots shot down over Germany. The information might be as simple as 'Why do P-51 fighters fire a short burst of tracer in air combat and then head for the UK?' This question would be incorporated into some innocent chatter – chatter which would show the prisoner how much the questioner already knew. Assuming he was giving nothing away – that the 'Krauts knew it already' – the pilot would let drop the critical information.

*A South Vietnamese soldier gives a drink to a female main force Viet Cong prisoner, captured with her AK after a fire fight. Correct prisoner handling will help the tactical questioner to do his job.*

# SEARCHING A PRISONER

*Two members of a fighting patrol from 40 Commando search their first prisoner. This Argentine marine, who had been directing aircraft into San Carlos Water, was one of the very few prisoners who had completely sanitised his kit: i.e. he had disposed of everything that could be of intelligence value. He found time to burn his maps, signals instructions and aide memoire, and smashed his radio after changing frequency from the operating frequency. No personal documentation of any kind was found on him.*

*You must be able to discriminate between the dross and those prisoners who will be of intelligence value. In addition to the prisoner's uniform, have a look at what weapons he is carrying. Anyone found with a Makarov pistol is probably worth investigating further.*

*This is the military identification document of a Soviet soldier killed in Afghanistan. In war every Warsaw Pact soldier with perhaps the exception of special purpose troops will carry one. This contains very useful information for the questioner.*

There are other techniques for questioning. The 'soft and hard' method may seem corny, but it can work. In this method, two questioners act out the roles of a harsh bully and a reasonable man. The reasonable man will enter the room as the hard man reaches the height of a tirade, and will eject him. Then he will apologise and sit down for a reasonable conversation with the prisoner.

### Don't get violent

Physical violence can be counter-productive. The fear or determination it produces can either make a prisoner too talkative and willing to agree to anything to stop the pain. Or violence can make a man silent – he may die in this state.

But verbal abuse, humiliation, sarcasm and all the verbal ploys that made schoolboys' and recruits' lives a misery can be used to full effect. Foul language can come as a shock to an officer who has been used to respect.

Almost as tiring to the questioner as to the prisoner is the constant repetition of the 'big four'. The prisoner is obliged to reply and so he can be provoked into bored anger by the droning questioner.

### Cold and discomfort

Since searching will have involved the removal of the prisoner's clothing as each garment is examined, there may be additional humiliation in standing semi-naked. It can certainly be very cold.

Prisoners will not be on a very substantial diet. Eating or drinking in his presence will add to his discomfort and can loosen his tongue.

Tactical questioning is hard work. It is not to be attempted by untrained men or women since in peace or war they could do damage.

# SOVIET ARMS OF SERVICE BADGES

The arm of service badge appears either on the right arm as a patch or as a dull cloth badge on the collars of the field uniform.

**1** Armoured corps

**2** Artillery

**3** Airborne

**4** Motor Rifle Regiment

**5** Chemical defence

**6** Signals

**7** Engineers

**8** Kommandants

# FIRST AID FOR BLOOD AND CHOKING AGENTS

## Choking agents

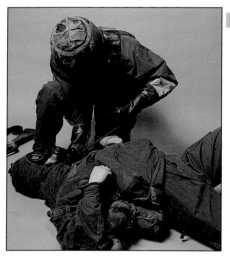

### CHECK YOUR PROTECTION

First make sure you and the casualty are adequately protected against chemical attack. Make sure you do not become the next casualty.

### KEEP HIM WARM

Put the casualty in a sleeping bag and keep him warm.

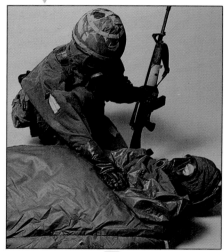

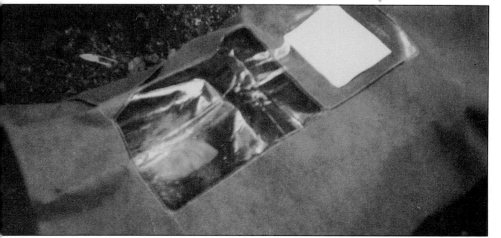

## Blood agents

*Blood agents kill by combining more readily than oxygen with the blood's haemoglobin in the lungs, starving the body of oxygen.* These agents are very volatile — that is, they evaporate very quickly and are therefore non-persistent. The most common blood agents are hydrogen cyanide (code letters AC) and cyanogen chloride (code CK). Hydrogen cyanide is a colourless gas with a smell of almonds. It is ideal for military use because it remains at lethal concentration only for a very limited period. It can therefore be used to bombard a position minutes before the attacking force arrives, inflicting casualties and forcing the defenders to mask up while the attacking force need wear no protection.

Blood agents attack the lungs and have a very rapid rate of action. *Don't,* therefore, take a last breath before you carry out the immediate action drill if there's a blood agent about. It will be your last!

## Choking agents

These kill by a process nicknamed 'dry land drowning'. They attack the breathing passages and the lungs, producing quantities of fluid in which you drown. They include:

**1** Chlorine

**2** Phosgene (code CG). This is a mixture of phosphorus and chlorine and smells vaguely of new mown hay. Chlorine and phosgene were used extensively in World War I. Both are non-persistent.

### USE CASUALTY BAG IF AVAILABLE

The casualty will be having difficulty in breathing as his lung capacity is diminished by fluid. If you have a casualty bag, put him in it and then unmask him. The casualty bag will protect him from any residual vapour hazard. Evacuate to medical aid as soon as possible.

# Blood agents

## Symptoms and treatment

| Agent | Treatment |
|---|---|
| **BLOOD (HCN)** | |
| Mild symptoms: headache, nausea, dizziness | Resuscitator or oxygen |
| Severe symptoms: increase in depth of breathing, violent convulsions, breathing stops in approx 1 min, death in 5 mins | Treatment at Regimental Aid Post |
| **CHOKING (phosgene)** | |
| Coughing and choking Tightness and pain in chest Nausea and vomiting Watering eyes (Possible latent period) 30 min – 24 hours) | Warmth Strict rest Treatment at Regimental Aid Post |

## CHECK YOUR PROTECTION

Blood agents are extremely non-persistent, but unless it is safe to do so you must make sure you both have sufficient protection should the attack continue. Later you may be able to unmask the casualty.

If you have no resuscitator and there is still a vapour hazard, then use the Holger-Nielsen method.

Keep checking to see whether the casualty has started breathing; if you continue once he is breathing you will do more damage.

## IF HE STOPS BREATHING, GIVE ARTIFICIAL RESPIRATION

The casualty may stop breathing, in which case you must give artificial respiration. If there is still a vapour hazard, remove his respirator and use the portable resuscitator.

## KEEP HIM WARM

## EVACUATE TO MEDICAL AID

Keep the casualty warm, put him in a sleeping bag and, if a casualty bag is available, place him in the bag and unmask him. Evacuate for further medical treatment.

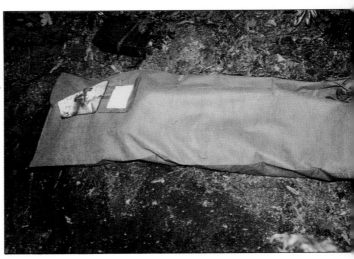

# FIRST AID FOR BLISTER AGENT

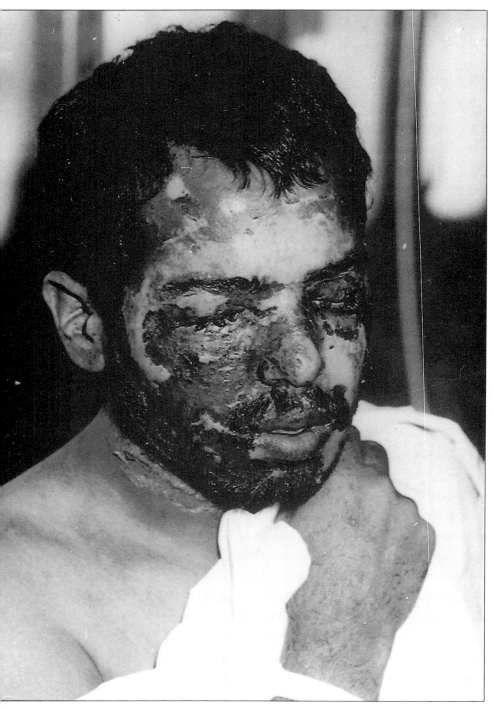

**Blister agents are classified in military terms as 'damaging agents' — but they can quite easily kill or cripple you, should you be heavily contaminated.** These agents cause inflammation and blistering of the skin, and concentrate on moist areas of the body. They can destroy contaminated internal tissues — for example, the lining of the lungs and the breathing passages. The blistering effect can be delayed for hours or even days in the case of sulphur mustard. You can take cover in a shell-hole or hollow in the ground and not notice the effects of mustard gas until you have become seriously injured by it.

## Types of blister agent

| Agent | Code |
|---|---|
| Sulphur mustard | HD |
| Lewisite | L |
| Mustard and Lewisite mix | HL |
| The Dicks group | D |
| Phosgene oxime | CX |

Mustard and mustard mixes are perhaps the most common agents and usually appear, after an airburst of some sort, as dark or yellow oily droplets that smell of garlic.

## Residual Vapour Hazard

These agents are very persistent and can hang around for weeks giving off vapour, leaving what is known as a residual vapour hazard. Such agents will usually be used in areas the enemy does not intend to use or move through himself. They are ideal for providing a permanent hazard in an enemy rear area (and forcing troops into NBC state Black), so that efficiency will be considerably reduced.

*An Iranian mustard gas casualty under treatment in the West. The Iraqis have used chemical weapons to great effect against Iranian massed attacks. Tissue damage is considerable, and is made significantly worse if any of the blisters burst.*

**1** Make sure you and the casualty are adequately protected. With a blister agent this means full protection, as they are always persistent and can continue as a contact hazard for at least 36 hours.

# Treatment for agent unknown

In any future European war it is very likely that the enemy will deploy agents of which we have little or no knowledge. As a result, you will probably be unable to recognise the agent from the casualties' symptoms. In such a case, it is vital that you evacuate the casualty to medical aid as quickly as possible.

**2** If you reach the casualty within five minutes of his being contaminated and agent has got into his eyes, you can flush it out with water. You must only do this within the first five minutes, as after that time the blisters will have started to form and rinsing with water may do more damage.

# Toxins

This is the growth area in chemical weapons; toxins are poisons produced by micro-organisms. They are chemical weapons from a biological source and are extremely toxic. They are likely to produce symptoms you won't recognise, and can range from lethal to incapacitating in their effect.

**3** Replace the respirator as soon as you have finished and check the casualty for reddening of the skin around the hairline, behind the ears, and on his hands. Immediately decontaminate any suspect areas with DKP 1. Swab off the powder with water.

**4** When you have decontaminated the skin of the affected area, dress the blisters with a shell dressing and then cover with a chemical-proof material such as the packing bags for the NBC suit. Do not break the blisters.

**5** As soon as you have decontaminated and dressed all the affected areas, evacuate the casualty for further medical aid.

# FIRST AID FOR MENTAL INCAPACITANTS

Symptoms of mental incapacitants can vary greatly from individual to individual. Some may look like they are suffering from battle shock, but others may go completely crazy and will have no perception of reality. In this state they may fire their weapon in all directions, pull pins on grenades, destroy equipment etc. Do not underestimate the effects of these agents.

*Mental incapacitants cause changes in individuals' behaviour patterns by affecting the brain.* The hallucinogens, such as LSD, affect different individuals in very different ways, so someone's behaviour after such an attack is difficult to predict.

These agents are more likely to be used against rear-area targets, as they can actually enhance the fighting ability of front line units. There are other, more predictable agents – such as Quinuclidinyl Benzilate (code BZ), which causes sleepiness, decreased alertness, and what appears to be increasing drunkenness.

## Physical incapacitants

These are designed not to kill, but to take you out of the battle – by making you feel so ill that you become ineffective, and put further pressure on the casevac system.

While not as dangerous as some of the mental incapacitants, these agents can cause conditions that will persist for hours or days after the original exposure. One example is Adamasite, which causes general vomiting, headache and weakness.

### CHECK YOUR PROTECTION

Check that you and the casualty are adequately protected. Remember, the casualty will not be rational and may attempt to remove his respirator or yours. You should always take on this type of casualty with someone else as they can be very difficult to subdue.

## MAKE SAFE HIS WEAPON

Make safe his weapon as soon as possible; he could kill you with it. Separate him also from anything else he could kill you or himself with, e.g. grenades, rockets etc. Continue to restrain him and never leave him on his own.

## GIVE HIM SOME WATER

Try to get the casualty to drink some water. If you cannot casevac him straight away he must always be guarded.

## RESTRAIN AND EVACUATE

If he is violent you may need to restrain him; if so, make sure he cannot injure himself on plasticuffs etc. If he has fits, make sure he does not swallow his tongue. Evacuate him to medical aid.

## Riot control agents

These are not classed as chemical agents, but do have a military use beyond riot control – for such tasks as smoking an enemy out of a bunker or tunnel, or when house clearing. Most work by irritating the respiratory tract and causing streaming eyes and smarting skin, especially in the more moist areas of the body. Victims usually recover completely soon after exposure to the agent has ceased.

# Snap Shooting with the Steyr

**The Austrian firm of Steyr-Mann-licher is best known for the futuristic AUG assault rifle, but it also produces a very successful 9-mm sub-machine-gun, the MPi 69.** An extremely robust weapon, the MPi 69 employs a wrap-around bolt like the UZI to reduce overall length while keeping a respectably long barrel. It is comfortable to grip, simple to operate and groups well firing single shots.

Steyr-Mannlicher GmbH is the latest title for a company which has been around since 1864, when it was founded by Josef Werndl to make

*Above: The cocking piece on the MPi 69 is the forward sling mount. The safety catch is a push-through type with three positions: 'safe' locks both the trigger and the bolt, half-way through permits single shots only; and pushing the safety bar all the way through means single shots on the first trigger pressure and full auto when you pull the trigger all the way back.*

*Left: The Steyr handles and shoots exceptionally well. The wraparound bolt, as with the UZI, means a decent length of pipe with short overall length. The only real problem is the cocking handle.*

rifles for the Austro-Hungarian army. It became the Waffenfabrik Steyr and when Austria was annexed by Germany in 1938 it was swallowed by the Hermann Goering Werke, was disgorged in 1945 to become Steyr-Daimler-Puch, and last year changed its title while remaining part of the S-D-P empire.

# Combat use of the sling

*The test model looks dangerous at first, in that when the weapon is loaded it could make itself ready and fire a round if the firer was carrying the weapon on the sling and, for example, jumped off the back of a truck.*

*The sling cocking device could be quite useful in some situations, where you need to go from load to ready at speed. When carrying the weapon across your body with a sling, all you have to do is knock the safety catch off and push the weapon away from you firmly.*

*The point of balance of the weapon is slightly forward of the pistol grip. Bursts over five rounds disappear off the target over the right shoulder. Bursts of two to three rounds can be kept on a Figure 11 at 25 m from the hip or underarm assault position with a little practice.*

*Left: The 'show clear' is a bit of a problem, as when the bolt is fully back it is difficult to see if the chamber is clear. Pulling the bolt back onto the second sear with a firm grip of the sling gives the best view of the chamber. Like all Steyr products, the weapon is very well made.*

In all that time rifles and pistols have been the company's principal products, but it has made two ventures into the sub-machine-gun business in the past. Its first venture is shrouded in mystery; there has been a brief mention of a design developed in 1918 by Steyr, few of which were made and all of which were destroyed by the Allied Disarmament Commission. Nothing exists at Steyr to confirm the former existence of this mysterious weapon, not even in its museum, and the company says, 'It's all in Leningrad, or somewhere . . . we were liberated by the Red Army.'

Steyr produced a much more successful weapon in 1930, the Steyr-Solothurn, so called because it was made by Steyr and marketed through a firm in Solothurn, Switzerland. In fact the design came from Rheinmetall of Germany, for whom the Solothurn firm was a 'front' organisation in the days when Germany was forbidden to make such weapons. It was a solid and reliable weapon, and was still in use in the mid-1970s with the Portuguese National Guard.

## A sound job

But in the 1960s Steyr decided to build a design of its own, since the time seemed ripe for a fresh look at sub-machine-guns. The weapon it produced was adopted by the Austrian army as the Maschinen Pistole 69 – MPi 69 – and has since been adopted in several other places. It is, like all Steyr products, a sound and workmanlike job, though it avoids the startling elements of design which make the Steyr AUG such a recognisable item.

*The sights are flip-up aperture rear sights for 100 and 200 m and a foresight post adjustable for windage and elevation. Both are protected by substantial steel ears.*

# Inside the Steyr

**Front sight**
The conventional post foresight is adjustable for windage and elevation, although a wide range of optical sights can be fitted by drilling the top of the body and adding sight mount bases.

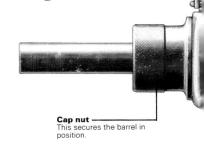

**Cap nut**
This secures the barrel in position.

The essentials of the MPi 69 are simple enough. A pressed-steel receiver, welded into a hollow box, carries a 260-mm barrel retained by a finger-tight nut at the front. The bolt is severely cut away so as to enclose the rear end of the barrel when forward, and has apertures to admit the cartridge and allow the empty case to be ejected. A single return spring is wrapped around a guide rod along which the bolt moves in recoil.

### Mags in the dark

There is a simple collapsible wire butt, and the magazine (25 or 32 shots) is inserted into the pistol grip. This latter is a good feature, since it makes changing magazines in the dark a great deal easier, as anyone who has ever tried changing a Sten or Thompson magazine in darkness will testify.

Like the AUG, the MPi 69 uses a two-stage trigger as a selector: a first pressure on the trigger gives single shots; pulling through against a stronger resistance fires full automatic at about 550 rounds per minute. Safety is provided by a cross-bolt catch: one end is marked 'S' in white and projects when the weapon is safe; the other is marked 'F' in red and pro-

*The weapon shoots very well on single-shot, producing 20-round zeroing groups well under 150 mm fired from kneeling at 25 m. There were no malfunctions with a wide variety of loads, from some very dodgy Yugoslavian sub-machine gun ammo from the 1960s to semi-jacketed soft point pistol ammunition.*

jects when in the firing condition.

Additional safety against accidental firing is provided by three safety notches in the breech-block; these are positioned so that dropping the gun butt-first and thus driving the bolt backwards will result in the first notch catching on the sear to prevent the bolt running forward and firing a round. The second notch is designed to catch the bolt in the case of a weak cartridge not providing enough impulse to drive the bolt back far enough to engage the normal firing notch in the sear. One way and another, accidental discharge of the Steyr is impossible.

The most novel feature, and one which arouses different opinions, is the method of cocking. The cocking handle is at the front left end of the receiver, and forms the forward attachment point for the sling, so that cocking the weapon is simply a matter of holding the pistol grip with one hand

The Steyr MPi 69, when introduced, was the first military weapon to be developed in Austria since the 1930s. The Steyr is a compact weapon which, like the UZI, has a long barrel but a short overall length. The bolt telescopes round the barrel for about two-thirds of the barrel length.

and jerking back the sling with the other. This is fine, as long as you don't try to loop the sling around your arm for steadiness when firing, which places tension on the cocking lever and prevents the bolt from closing, so the gun will fail to fire. Leave the sling free and you'll have no trouble.

### Firing port model

To cater for those who dislike this system, the MPi 81 was developed; this is exactly the same weapon except that the sling is attached to a con-

---

# Field stripping the Steyr MPi 69

**1** After clearing the weapon, let the bolt forward under control and release the cap nut locking button which is on the right of the front sight. This will allow you to unscrew the cap nut which holds the barrel in position.

**2** Remove the cap nut and then pull the barrel assembly out from the frame forwards. This is exactly the same procedure as on the UZI and the Beretta PM12.

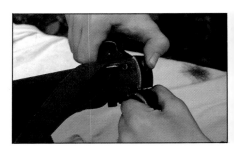

**3** To remove the working parts, locate the takedown button, which protrudes through and locks a hinged plate covering the back of the body. Press in on the button and rotate the plate upwards.

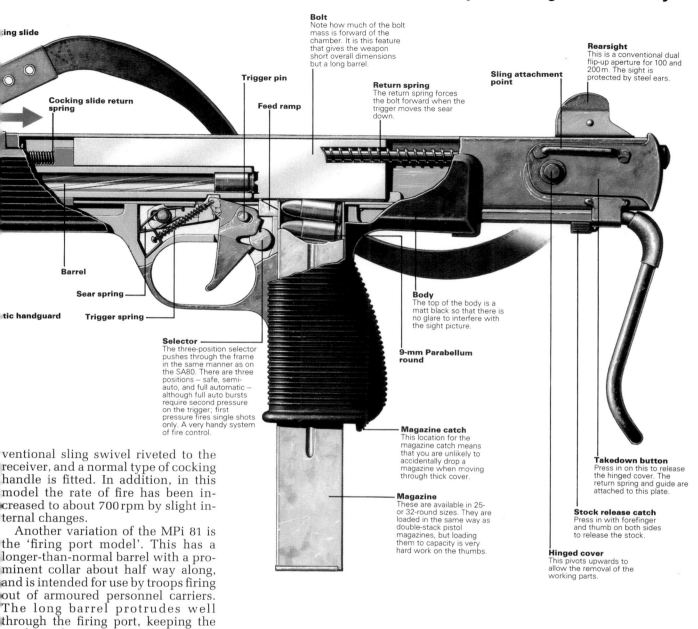

**ing slide**

**Cocking slide return spring**

**Barrel**

**Sear spring**

**tic handguard**

**Trigger spring**

**Trigger pin**

**Feed ramp**

**Bolt**
Note how much of the bolt mass is forward of the chamber. It is this feature that gives the weapon short overall dimensions but a long barrel.

**Return spring**
The return spring forces the bolt forward when the trigger moves the sear down.

**Sling attachment point**

**Rearsight**
This is a conventional dual flip-up aperture for 100 and 200 m. The sight is protected by steel ears.

**Body**
The top of the body is a matt black so that there is no glare to interfere with the sight picture.

**9-mm Parabellum round**

**Selector**
The three-position selector pushes through the frame in the same manner as on the SA80. There are three positions – safe, semi-auto, and full automatic – although full auto bursts require second pressure on the trigger; first pressure fires single shots only. A very handy system of fire control.

**Magazine catch**
This location for the magazine catch means that you are unlikely to accidentally drop a magazine when moving through thick cover.

**Magazine**
These are available in 25- or 32-round sizes. They are loaded in the same way as double-stack pistol magazines, but loading them to capacity is very hard work on the thumbs.

**Takedown button**
Press in on this to release the hinged cover. The return spring and guide are attached to this plate.

**Stock release catch**
Press in with forefinger and thumb on both sides to release the stock.

**Hinged cover**
This pivots upwards to allow the removal of the working parts.

ventional sling swivel riveted to the receiver, and a normal type of cocking handle is fitted. In addition, in this model the rate of fire has been increased to about 700 rpm by slight internal changes.

Another variation of the MPi 81 is the 'firing port model'. This has a longer-than-normal barrel with a prominent collar about half way along, and is intended for use by troops firing out of armoured personnel carriers. The long barrel protrudes well through the firing port, keeping the smoke and gases out of the vehicle,

**4** Take hold of the return spring and guide, which is connected to the bolt, and pull the whole assembly out of the back of the body. You should not strip the weapon further in the field.

**5** You can remove the body from the plastic fore-end and pistol grip by pulling the body to the rear. However, you must support the cocking piece while you do this as it is a very fiddly job to reassemble the cocking piece and spring.

**6** The weapon field-stripped shows a remarkable resemblance to the UZI. Reassembly is in reverse order: be careful when placing the metal body back into the plastic fore-end, as it is the plastic fore-end that holds the cocking piece of the sling in place.

*The magazine release is a heel of the butt catch, which actually works very well and reduces the chances of your accidentally dropping the magazine. This can happen if the magazine catch is on the flat side of the weapon.*

*The telescoping butt has a release catch underneath the hinged cover. Pinch in on both sides to release it until it locks. An interesting feature is that the stock will lock in three different positions to suit the arm length of the firer.*

and the collar lodges on to the sill of the port and prevents the weapon accidentally being drawn inside if the vehicle lurches during firing. It is also fitted with the 1.4× optical sight of the AUG rifle, carried in special brackets at the rear of the receiver, a position which allows the sight to be used behind a vision block above the firing port.

### Sound suppressor

It is possible to fit a sound suppressor to the MPi 69 or to the standard MPi 81, by simply unscrewing the retaining nut and removing the barrel, then inserting a special barrel and suppressor unit, the latter screwing on

# Battlefield Evaluation: comparing

## MPi 69

New sub-machine gun designs have appeared and disappeared with bewildering rapidity in the last 20 years, but the Steyr MPi 69 and 81 have established themselves as capable and reliable weapons. In service with various police and paramilitary units in Europe as well as the Austrian army, it is pleasant to shoot, easy to field strip and has no significant vices.

**Specification:**
**Cartridge:** 9mm×19 Parabellum
**Weight:** 3.55kg with 32-round magazine
**Length:** 465mm (butt retracted)
**Muzzle velocity:** 381 metres per second
**Cyclic rate of fire:** 550 rounds per minute
**Magazine:** 25- or 32-round box

**Assessment**
| | |
|---|---|
| Reliability | **** |
| Accuracy | **** |
| Age | *** |
| Worldwide users | ** |

*The Steyr shoots very well, but there has been a lot of competition from Beretta and UZI.*

## PA3-DM

This is the locally produced SMG used by the Argentine army; many were captured in the Falklands. A blowback-operated gun with a wrap-around bolt, the body is a metal pressing which gives the weapon a decidedly 'under-the-counter' appearance. The extended stock is based on the sliding butt of the old US M3 SMG. Firing single shot or full auto, the PA3-DM has a chunky fire-selector above the pistol grip and a grip-safety.

**Specification:**
**Cartridge:** 9mm×19 Parabellum
**Weight:** 3.95kg (with 25-round magazine)
**Length:** 523mm with butt retracted
**Muzzle velocity:** 400 metres per second
**Cyclic rate of fire:** 650 rounds per minute
**Magazine:** 25-round box

**Assessment**
| | |
|---|---|
| Reliability | *** |
| Accuracy | *** |
| Age | *** |
| Worldwide users | * |

*This Argentine offering uses the same wrap-around bolt system as the UZI and Steyr.*

## 9mm F1

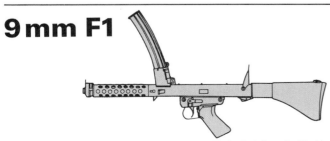

The standard SMG of the Australian army since 1962, the F1 follows its World War II predecessor, the Owen, in having a vertical magazine. The pistol grip is from the L1A1 SLR and the cocking handle also duplicates the position and action of that on the SLR. A bracket for the sling swivel prevents you accidentally getting your left hand too close to the muzzle.

**Specification:**
**Cartridge:** 9mm×19 Parabellum
**Weight:** 4.3kg
**Length:** 714mm
**Muzzle velocity:** 366 metres per second
**Cyclic rate of fire:** 600-640 rounds per minute
**Magazine:** 34-round box

**Assessment**
| | |
|---|---|
| Reliability | ***** |
| Accuracy | **** |
| Age | **** |
| Worldwide users | * |

*The F1 Aust is developed from the Owen gun and larger than the wrap-around bolt designs.*

to the receiver and acting as the retaining nut. This is a very efficient assembly, reducing the noise by something like 30dB and still allowing full automatic fire.

Firing the MPi 69 is much the same as firing any other sub-machine-gun; it has no vices, is as accurate as you have any right to expect, and never seems to give any trouble. The firing port model is remarkably accurate due to its longer barrel and optical sight, though it is hardly the weapon for street-fighting. The MPi 69 may lack the glamour of some other designs, but Steyr has been producing it now for 20 years without complaints, and it looks like continuing.

*When shooting, remember that you cannot use the sling as a support as it will prevent the bolt closing properly and cause a jam. The magazines are standard staggered-row box magazines, available in 25- or 32-round sizes.*

*The magazines are difficult to fill to capacity, so use a magazine filling tool. When filled the magazines are quite difficult to engage in the magazine housing. Cock the weapon and set the safety catch before putting the mag on.*

# the Steyr with its rivals

## Star Z-84

The Spanish Z-84 makes extensive use of steel stampings and fires from an open bolt. Its feed system is designed to cope with hollow-point and semi-jacketed rounds as well as standard military FMJ. There are no external moving parts, the cocking handle goes forward under spring power and remains still during firing. The centre of gravity is right above the pistol grip so you can theoretically fire it one-handed during an emergency.

**Specification:**
**Cartridge:** 9mm×19 Parabellum
**Weight:** 3kg unloaded
**Length:** 410mm (stock retracted)
**Muzzle velocity:** 400 metres per second
**Cyclic rate of fire:** 600 rounds per minute
**Magazine:** 25-round box

**Assessment**
| | |
|---|---|
| Reliability | **** |
| Accuracy | **** |
| Age | * |
| Worldwide users | * |

*The Star Z-84 makes maximum use of steel stampings to produce a cheap but effective SMG.*

## Sterling Para pistol

The 9mm Mk 7 is a cut-down version of the Sterling SMG designed for use in confined spaces. Sold to several navies and US police departments, it is available in several versions. The C4 and C8 models are semi-automatic, firing from a closed bolt which is much more accurate than the open-bolt A4 and A8 versions. The C4 and A4 have 89-mm barrels; the C8 and A8, 198-mm.

**Specification:**
(Mk 7 A4)
**Cartridge:** 9mm×19 Parabellum
**Weight:** 2.2kg (empty)
**Length:** 355mm
**Muzzle velocity:** undisclosed
**Cyclic rate of fire:** 550 rounds per minute
**Magazine:** 10-, 15- or 34-round box

**Assessment**
| | |
|---|---|
| Reliability | **** |
| Accuracy | ** |
| Age | ** |
| Worldwide users | * |

*The Sterling is the size of some of the smaller wrap-around bolt SMGs, but has about half the barrel length.*

## PPSh-41

This standard Soviet World War II SMG is not strictly comparable with the MPi 69, but it is interesting to see how sub-machine gun design has progressed since 1945. The PPSh was widely supplied to pro-Soviet forces during the 1950s in the same way as the AK-47 series are now. Chambered for the 7.62-mm cartridge now supplanted by 9-mm Parabellum, the PPSh was a brutally simple, soldier-proof weapon. They were last encountered during the Rhodesian war but have now been replaced by Kalashnikovs even in the farthest reaches of the bush.

**Specification:**
**Cartridge:** 7.62mm
**Weight:** 5.69kg with 71-round magazine
**Length:** 780mm
**Muzzle velocity:** 488 metres per second
**Cyclic rate of fire:** 800 rounds per minute
**Magazine:** 71-round drum

**Assessment**
| | |
|---|---|
| Reliability | **** |
| Accuracy | *** |
| Age | ***** |
| Worldwide users | ** |

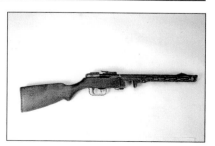

*The PPsh 41 was a very popular weapon on both sides on the Eastern Front.*

# Marauding with the Marder

**When the Marder entered service with the West German Army in 1971 it represented not only a breakthrough in military technology but also an enormous improvement in the capabilities of the Bundeswehr.** The Marder was the first Mechanised Infantry Combat Vehicle (MICV) to enter NATO service. Unlike the contemporary NATO APCs which were designed simply to ferry troops into action, the Marder enabled West German infantry to fight supported by the heavy armament of their vehicle.

## Development

Marder took nearly fifteen years to develop. In the late 1950s a chassis was developed which could be utilised for a number of basic vehicles including the Jagdpanzer Kanone and Jagdpanzer Rakete tank destroyers, a light reconnaissance tank and an MICV.

Priority was given to the Jagdpanzer Kanone which entered production in 1965 and then to the Jadgpanzer Rakete so that construction of the MICV was delayed until 1967, and the reconnaissance tank was eventually abandoned.

Troop trials for the MICV ran from October 1968 to April of the following year after which the vehicle was formally adopted and named Marder. Production lines were established at Kassel and MaK of Kiel and an initial order for 2,801 vehicles was placed. However by the time that production was completed in 1975 this number had been increased to 3,111.

The all-welded hull of the Marder provides the crew of four and six passengers with protection from small arms fire and shell splinters with the front of the vehicle affording complete protection against up to 20mm projectiles.

The driver, seated at the front left of the hull, has a single piece hatch-cover opening to the right and is equipped with three periscopes, the centre of which can be replaced by a passive night driving device for operating closed down. An infantryman, usually the section commander,

*The Bundeswehr was the first NATO army to introduce an MICV. Marder entered service 12 years ahead of the American M2 Bradley and 17 years before the British Army acquired Warrior. The well-sloped glacis will stop a 20-mm cannon shell.*

equipped with a single hatch-cover opening to the right but in this instance supported by a single periscope capable of 360 degree traverse, is seated behind the driver.

The six infantrymen in the troop compartment at the rear are carried in comparative comfort, seated three aside and back-to-back to enable them to fire on the move. Two MOWAG-designed spherical firing ports are built into each side of the troop compartment, as are two circular hatches and three periscopes into the roof.

## Mobility

Powered by an MTU MB 833 Ea-500 6-cylinder liquid-cooled diesel engine positioned to the right of the driver, the Marder can develop a useful 600hp at 2,200 rpm. A Renk four-speed HSWL-194 planetry gearbox and stepless hydrostatic steering unit,

The infantry fire *G3* rifles from their roof hatches. They can also fire from within the vehicle using the firing ports in the hull side. A ventilation system clears away the fumes far more efficiently than in the Soviet BMP.

West German infantry dismount via the power-operated ramp in the hull rear. During World War II the Germans developed their distinctive style of infantry/armour operations, using half-track APCs in combination with tanks. *Marder's* development as an MICV owes much to German tactical experience in World War II.

transmitting power to the tracks via two final drive assemblies mounted at the front of the hull, combine to give the Marder a top speed of 75 kph (47 mph) forwards or backwards.

With a maximum road range of 520 km (325 miles) coupled with the ability to climb gradients of 60 per cent and to ford to depths of 2.5 metres (8 feet) the Marder has excellent mobility, despite its size.

## Firepower

Produced by KUKA of Augsburg the two-man forward mounted turret is among the most advanced of its type. The commander and gunner mounted on the left and right respectively each has a single piece hatch-cover and adjustable seat. Turret traverse and gun elevation are operated electro-hydraulically, whilst loading and un-loading, cocking, firing and re-loading

are all executed under armour protection.

The 20-mm Rheinmetall Mk 20 Rh 202 cannon is fed via a series of rigid and flexible chutes from three different belts to give the gunner a choice of either Armour Piercing or High Explosive shells.

A dual control system enables the commander to over-ride the gunner in the case of an emergency whilst the turret itself can be operated manually via a series of mechanical gear boxes and the gun fired by foot controls in the case of a failure in the hydraulic or electrical systems. To avoid fumes and clutter, empty cartridge cases are ejected automatically outside the turret.

Since 1982 most Marders have been improved by the retro-fitting of a double belt feed for the 20-mm cannon, improved night capabilities

*Marder* on the move with hatches open: the position behind the driver is occupied by one of the infantrymen, who dismounts to fight. The height of *Marder* (nearly three metres) is readily apparent. The Soviet BMP is just 2.15 m high.

*Marder has a unique sting in the tail: the box above the hull rear houses a remotely controlled MG3 7.62-mm machine-gun. This traverses 180 degrees to cover the whole rear arc and can elevate to +60 degrees.*

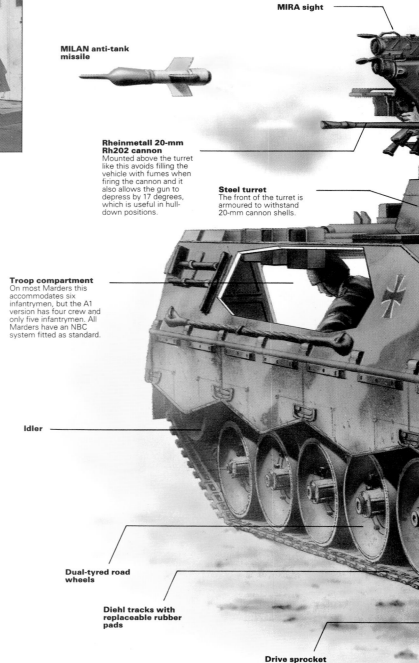

**MILAN anti-tank missile**

**MIRA sight**

**Rheinmetall 20-mm Rh202 cannon**
Mounted above the turret like this avoids filling the vehicle with fumes when firing the cannon and it also allows the gun to depress by 17 degrees, which is useful in hull-down positions.

**Steel turret**
The front of the turret is armoured to withstand 20-mm cannon shells.

**Troop compartment**
On most Marders this accommodates six infantrymen, but the A1 version has four crew and only five infantrymen. All Marders have an NBC system fitted as standard.

**Idler**

**Dual-tyred road wheels**

**Diehl tracks with replaceable rubber pads**

**Drive sprocket**

and an enhanced image intensifier with thermal pointer.

A MOWAG-designed remote-controlled 7.62-mm MG 3 machine-gun mounted above the rear of the crew compartment gives the Marder a unique sting in the tail.

With the exception of command vehicles, all Marders in West German service are fitted with a Euromissile MILAN ATGW launcher.

## Variants

A number of early variants of the Marder were cancelled either as being ineffective or too expensive and were subsequently replaced by derivations of the less complex and far cheaper United States' M 113 APC. Others were, however, proceeded with and are presently operational.

After strenuous competition between Rheinmetall and Mauser for the production of a new 25-mm cannon to replace the present 20-mm Rheinmetall system the latter proved successful and has recently been awarded a

*A top view of Marder reveals the three roof periscopes which allow everyone in the troop compartment to see out. The commander's hatch on the right-hand side of the turret is clearly visible.*

development contract to retro-fit their Mauser E into the existing KUKA turret. In addition to firing HE and AP ammunition, the Mauser will accept an Armour-Piercing Fin-Stabilised Discarding Sabot (APFSDS) round capable of penetrating the armour of the latest Soviet BMP. Although, due to financial constraints, the new cannon will not become fully operational for several years, its very existence guarantees the continuation of the Marder into the twenty-first century.

A small number of Radarpanzer TURs (Tiefflieger Uberwachungs Radar) entered service in 1981. Con-

sisting basically of a Siemens radar with a range of some 30 km (18.5 miles) attached to an hydraulically operated arm, the base of which is itself welded to an extensively modified turretless Marder chassis, the TUR has a crew of four and is armed with two 7.62-mm machine-guns for local defence.

The Bundeswehr also uses the Marder chassis to mount the highly successful Euromissile Roland 2 Surface-to-Air missile developed jointly with France. Two missiles are carried in the ready-to-use position, with a further eight stowed internally. With a maximum range of 6,300 metres,

**Commander**
The commander and gunner both have PERI Z11 sights offering ×2 and ×6 magnification. The Marder A1 is fitted with an image intensifier.

**Co-axial MG3 7.62 mm machine gun**
Marder carries 5,000 rounds of 7.62-mm ammunition for the co-axial and remote controlled machine-guns.

**Smoke dischargers**

**Gunner**
The 20-mm cannon is served by three separate belts so the gunner can rapidly alter his choice of ammunition as different targets appear.

**Driver**
The driver has three periscopes, one of which can be replaced by a night vision device.

**Engine compartment**
The MTU MB 833 six-cylinder liquid-cooled diesel developes 600 hp at 2300 rpm.

# Inside the Marder

Entering service in 1971, the Marder was a far more capable vehicle than the M113 APCs widely used by the Bundeswehr. Compared with the Soviet BMP series, the Marder was large and lacked anti-tank capability, but has now been fitted with MILAN.

minimum range of 500 metres and radar range of 18 km, the Schulzen-panzer Roland, of which 140 examples are in service, provides an excellent companion to the twin bar-relled 30-mm Gepard, itself one of the best anti-aircraft gunnery systems in NATO service.

To meet Argentinian requirements, Thyssen Henschel has developed the TAM (Tanque Argentino Mediano)

*Marder at speed with the commander clinging to the rim of his hatch. Despite being two or three times as heavy as many APCs, the Marder has a good power-to-weight ratio and excellent battlefield mobility.*

Medium Tank of which 300 have recently been built under licence. Equipped with a more powerful 720 hp engine, less sophisticated 20-mm cannon and a 7.62-mm anti-aircraft machine-gun the TAM is in most other respects similar to the Marder and is itself proving a great success as a "parent" vehicle for a large series of variants.

Since 1982 most Marders have been up-graded to either A1 or A1A status. Stowage and storage have been

*Marder is not amphibious but can ford up to 1.5 metres without preparation. Here it uses its deep wading kit, distinguished by the schnorkel to the right of the turret. This copes with a depth of 2.5 metres.*

# Battlefield Evaluation: comparing

## Marder

The West Germans were not far behind the Soviets in introducing an APC which was a fighting vehicle in itself as opposed to an armoured transport. Entering service in 1968, the Marder's powerful armament is looking rather dated for the 1990s, but it has lasted better than the BMP-1.

**Specification:**
**Crew:** 4+6
**Combat weight:** 29 tonnes
**Road speed:** 75 km/h
**Power to weight ratio:** 20.5 hp/tonne
**Length:** 6.79 m
**Height:** 2.98 m
**Armament:** 1×20-mm cannon; 2×7.62-mm machine-guns

**Assessment**
Firepower ★★★
Protection ★★★
Age ★★★
Worldwide users ★

*Marder's excellent cross-country performance enables it to keep up with West Germany's Leopard tanks.*

## Saurer 4K 4FA

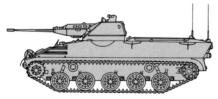

Only in service with the Austrian army, the Saurer 4K series includes a basic APC model armed with a single .50-cal machine-gun and the Grenadier Schutzenpanzer version which sports a 20-mm cannon. The APC is proof against small-arms fire and the front will keep out 20-mm cannon. Mortar-carrying and ambulance versions are also available.

**Specification:** (20-mm cannon version)
**Crew:** 2+8
**Combat weight:** 15 tonnes
**Road speed:** 65 km/h
**Power to weight ratio:** 16.6 hp/tonne
**Length:** 5.4 m
**Height:** 1.65 m
**Armament:** 1×20-mm cannon

**Assessment**
Firepower ★★
Protection ★★
Age ★★★★
Worldwide users ★

*Production of the Saurer finished in 1969. A year later the company was taken over by Steyr-Daimler-Puch.*

## YW 531

Developed in the late 1960s, this Chinese APC has seen action in Vietnam, Uganda (the Tanzanians use them) and in Angola by Zairean forces in 1976. It is a straightforward 1960s design: an armoured box with a 12.7-mm machine-gun on top. Ambulance, command post and 120-mm mortar-carrying versions are also produced.

**Specification:**
**Crew:** 4+10
**Combat weight:** 12.6 tonnes
**Road speed:** 65 km/h
**Power to weight ratio:** 25 hp/tonne
**Length:** 5.4 m
**Height:** 2.5 m
**Armament:** 1×12.7-mm machine-gun

**Assessment**
Firepower ★
Protection ★★
Age ★★★
Worldwide users ★★★★

*The YW 531 APC is also used to provide the chassis for SP mortars and the Type 70 MRL.*

improved, flaps fitted to the periscopes and the commander's external NBC system for utilisation when firing the MILANs modernised. The crew of four has been retained but the number of passengers reduced to five.

Despite its age, Marder is still an excellent fighting vehicle and remains the equal of such later systems as the British Warrior and United States' Bradley. It will clearly play an important role in West German military strategy for many years to come.

*Having backed his vehicle into the trees, this Marder commander prepares to fire MILAN. All West German army Marders are now fitted with MILAN except their command vehicles.*

# the Marder with its rivals

## Pansarbandvagn 302

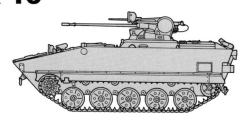

The Swedish army was one of the first to fit a cannon to its standard APC: the Pbv 302 entered service in 1966. Fully amphibious, it has a small turret on the left-hand side fitted with a 20-mm Hispano Suiza cannon which fires HE and AP ammunition. The front of the vehicle is proof against 20-mm cannon fire and the double-skinned hull gives added buoyancy and protection against HEAT rounds.

**Specification:**
**Crew:** 2+10
**Combat weight:** 13.5 tonnes
**Road speed:** 66 km/h
**Power to weight ratio:** 21 hp/tonne
**Length:** 5.35 m
**Height:** 2.5 m to turret top
**Armament:** 1×20-mm cannon

**Assessment**
Firepower    ★★★
Protection    ★★★
Age    ★★★
Worldwide users  ★

*The Pbv 302 was more heavily armed than most APCs appearing during the early 1960s.*

## AMX-10

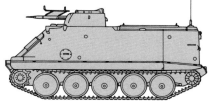

The AMX-10 followed the by then established pattern for an 'Infantry Fighting Vehicle' with a cannon armament firing AP shells to chew up opposing APCs. The vehicle serves as the basis for a large number of specialist versions and has proved highly popular in the export market.

**Specification:**
**Crew:** 3+8
**Combat weight:** 14.5 tonnes
**Road speed:** 65 km/h
**Power to weight ratio:** 20 hp/tonne
**Length:** 5.78 m
**Height:** 2.57 m
**Armament:** 1×20-mm cannon; 1×7.62-mm machine-gun

**Assessment**
Firepower    ★★
Protection    ★★★
Age    ★★★
Worldwide users  ★★★

*The AMX-10 is a capable MICV but not the equal of Warrior or the Bradley.*

## MCV-80 Warrior

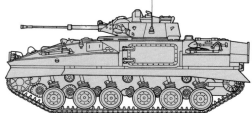

Although Warrior is entering service this year, its impact on the British tactics has not yet become clear. The Germans have years of experience in Panzergrenadier tactics but it is unlikely that the British will follow the same sort of tactical plan as the Bundeswehr.

**Specification:**
**Crew:** 3+7
**Combat weight:** 24.5 tonnes
**Road speed:** 75 km/h
**Power to weight ratio:** 22.5 hp/tonne
**Length:** 6.34 m
**Height:** 2.73 m
**Armament:** 1×30-mm cannon; 1×7.62-mm machine-gun

**Assessment**
Firepower    ★★★★
Protection    ★★★
Age    ★★
Worldwide users  ★

*The fastest tracked vehicle in NATO, Warrior is the best of the new generation of MICVs.*

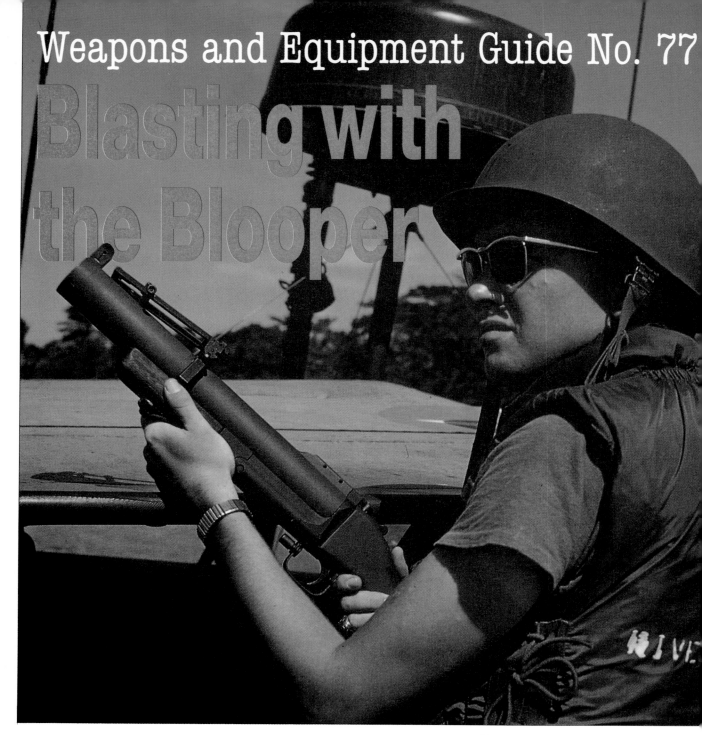

# Blasting with the Blooper

**The traditional way of sending a grenade a long distance is to launch it from a rifle, and there is still a lot to be said for this system.** A well-designed rifle grenade should be able to reach 350-400 metres' range and deliver a useful destructive effect at the target.

Moreover, it can do this without putting excessive strain on the rifle or the man firing it, and no longer demands special blank ammunition to be laboriously loaded into the rifle. Modern rifle grenades are fitted with highly efficient bullet traps in their tail units, so that the grenade can be slipped over the rifle muzzle and

launched using any cartridge the rifleman happens to have loaded in the chamber or ready in his magazine – ball, AP, tracer, whatever comes along.

## Shoulder busters

This was not always the case: 30 years ago, rifle grenades were at the bottom of their popularity curve and most armies had completely abandoned them. This was mostly because the designs of the time were generally leftovers from World War II and were so heavy that they had a tendency to shake the semi-automatic rifles of the period to pieces. The present position

*Nasty experiences fighting the Viet Cong armed with B-40 or RPG-2 rocket launchers soon taught the US Army the value of a grenade launcher capable of lobbing high explosive grenades accurately out to 350m. The M79 was the answer, seen here in use on a Navy PBR.*

of the rifle grenade is entirely due to research and development carried out by private manufacturers; government development has been practically zero.

So in the absence of rifle grenades, and with very little enthusiasm, the Americans in Vietnam were faced with something of a problem when the soldiers demanded a powerful anti-

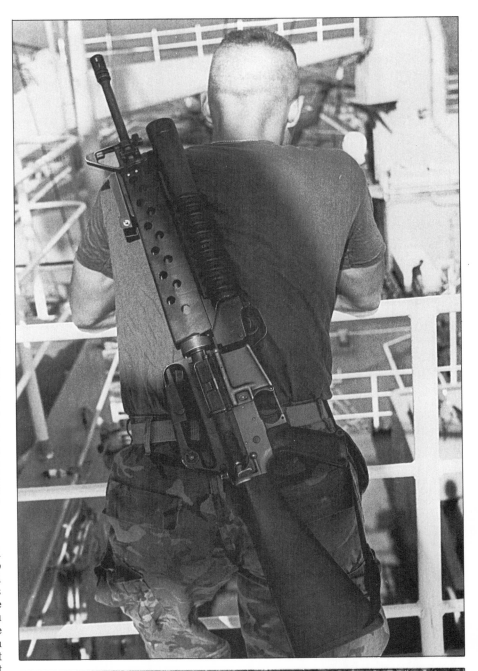

*The current US Army 40-mm grenade launcher is the excellent M203 which has been adopted by many forces. The M203 can be fitted on anything from a FAL to an AKM.*

ambush weapon. The rifle grenade would have been the ideal answer, allowing an ambushed column to give rapid high-explosive response to a range capable of dealing with all the elements of a jungle ambush. But they hadn't got a decent grenade, and had more or less abandoned the grenade-launching concept.

### High-tech rifle plan

In the 1950s, the US Army was bubbling with new ideas for infantry weapons, one of which was SPIW – the Special Purpose Individual Weapon. This was to be a high-tech rifle with sundry attachments making it capable of doing everything from demolishing bunkers to bringing down stratospheric bombers – at least, if you believed all the hype that went on at the time.

But one idea that came along was of making an attachment which would allow special grenades to be launched. To do this you had to have a grenade, and so the design departments developed a 40-mm high explosive grenade fitted into a cartridge case. By the time they had this working, SPIW had gone the way of all flesh, and so a weapon now became necessary: this led to the M79 launcher.

### Shotgun landing

The M79 was a simple single-barrel weapon, the barrel dropping down to load just like a shotgun. Once loaded and closed, the firer put it to his shoulder, took aim through a simple open sight, and pulled the trigger. You might expect that firing a hefty little grenade from a lightweight weapon would give you some problems, but the ammunition design was such that the whole thing became very controllable and consistent.

The designers revived a principle originated by the Germans during World War II, called the 'High-Low Pressure System'. In this, the propelling charge is confined inside a small chamber in the base of the cartridge case, this chamber being provided with carefully calculated holes. When the cap is fired, the charge explodes

*To load and fire the M203, simply press in the barrel latch on the left-hand side and slide the barrel forward to insert the round, then slide it back until it locks. Move the safety catch inside the trigger guard back to put the weapon on safe.*

1541

inside this chamber and develops a very high pressure – in the region of $2500\,kg/cm^2$. This, without some form of control, would blow the grenade out of the weapon at colossal speed and place an extremely high pressure on the weapon breech. But the high pressure is confined to the special chamber in the cartridge case and via the specially-designed holes 'bleeds' into the empty space of the rest of the cartridge case.

Here it expands and the pressure drops to about $200\,kg/cm^2$, enough to send the grenade out at about 76 m/sec velocity and to a range of 350-400 metres, yet without placing excessive pressure on the body of the weapon. This enables the barrel to be thin in section and thus light in weight, without hazarding safety.

## Achilles heel

The original grenade was a high explosive type; the grenade body was of thin sheet metal and concealed a spherical pre-fragmented grenade containing explosive and, in front of it, an impact fuse. This was the Achilles heel of the entire system, since to obtain certainty of action and yet keep the grenade safe until it had been fired, the fuse was somewhat

# Inside the M79

Simple, reliable and accurate, the M79 has seen action from Vietnam to South Armagh and will continue in service around the world for some years to come despite the introduction of under-barrel grenade launchers.

**Barrel**
The 'high low pressure system' in the cartridges avoids unacceptably high pressures enabling the barrel and breech to be of relatively light construction. The whole weapon weighs only 1.63kg loaded. The barrel is rifled to spin stabilise the grenades and the rotating motion acts on the grenade fuse to arm the grenade at a safe distance from the firer.

**Foresight**
This consists of a tapered blade with protective ears. With the rearsight flipped down you still have fixed sights that are good for up to 100 metres.

**Rearsight**
The rearsight has a spring-loaded lock that will hold it in either position. There is a windage screw on the right-hand side. One click moves the impact of the grenade 28cms at 200 metres; turn it clockwise to adjust the impact to the right.

**40mm M 79 HE grenade**
The grenade has a casualty radius of 5 m means that 50% of unprotected personn circle of radius 5 m fr the point of detonatic become casualties. T casualty radius may I limited but the accur with which the grena can be placed makes for this.

**Elevation scale and lock screw**
Elevation is graduated from 75 to 375 metres in 25-m increments. As the rearsight is moved up the scale it is cammed slightly to the left to compensate for the slightly rightward drift of the grenade at longer ranges.

**Sling swivel**

**Fore end assembl**

**Takedown screw**
In most circumstances all you have to do for normal daily cleaning is to break the weapon open. If you have immersed the weapon in water you may need to strip it completely, starting by removing the

screw in the rear-mounting hole of the sling swivel. This will allow you to remove the fore end assembly by pulling it down until it clears the lug on the sight base and then forwards to remove it.

*Special forces have always been keen on customising their weapons to suit their task and the Vietnamese obviously shared this preoccupation, as this cut-down M79 shows. Flechette rounds were available at this time, which probably made this shorty the ultimate in sidearms for personal protection.*

complex and took up more space inside the grenade body than the actual explosive component. A simpler fuse would have allowed a heavier explosive charge and thus a more lethal grenade, but at the price of reduced safety.

## Choice of loads

Since the first grenades were developed, many variant models have appeared so that there is now a wide range of options including shaped charge for attacking light armour, high explosive/fragmentation for anti-personnel tasks, and smoke and flare for signalling. There have also been buck-shot and flechette loadings in the past, though these have been dropped from the inventory.

The M79 served its purpose as an anti-ambush weapon, and then was integrated into the infantry section as a useful light support weapon. But there were complaints that it was a 'dedicated' weapon and demanded a dedicated user – a man armed with the M79 was OK for firing grenades but has no purpose in life other than that, and was unable to defend himself or act as part of the rifle squad.

## Clamp-on launcher

So Colt decided to develop a clamp-on launcher which would fit under the barrel of the M16 rifle and allow the man to fire either his rifle or a grenade, as the situation demanded. In fact, it was harking back to the SPIW concept. The first model was effective but not very reliable, and it was subsequently improved into the

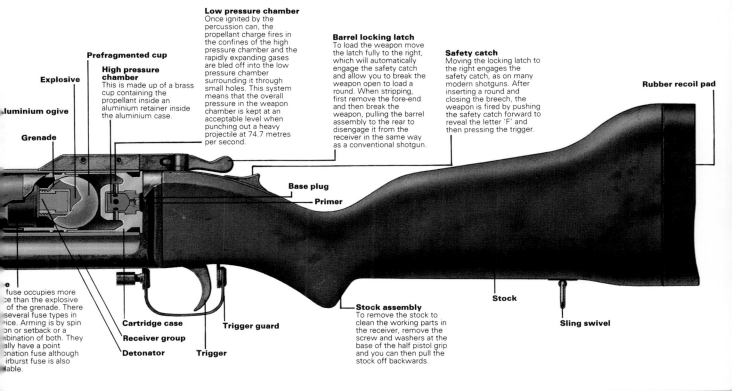

**Prefragmented cup**

**Explosive**

**Aluminium ogive**

**Grenade**

**High pressure chamber**
This is made up of a brass cup containing the propellant inside an aluminium retainer inside the aluminium case.

**Low pressure chamber**
Once ignited by the percussion can, the propellant charge fires in the confines of the high pressure chamber and the rapidly expanding gases are bled off into the low pressure chamber surrounding it through small holes. This system means that the overall pressure in the weapon chamber is kept at an acceptable level when punching out a heavy projectile at 74.7 metres per second.

**Barrel locking latch**
To load the weapon move the latch fully to the right, which will automatically engage the safety catch and allow you to break the weapon open to load a round. When stripping, first remove the fore-end and then break the weapon, pulling the barrel assembly to the rear to disengage it from the receiver in the same way as a conventional shotgun.

**Safety catch**
Moving the locking latch to the right engages the safety catch, as on many modern shotguns. After inserting a round and closing the breech, the weapon is fired by pushing the safety catch forward to reveal the letter 'F' and then pressing the trigger.

**Rubber recoil pad**

**Base plug**

**Primer**

...fuse occupies more ...ce than the explosive ...of the grenade. There ...several fuse types in ...vice. Arming is by spin ...on or setback or a ...bination of both. They ...ally have a point ...onation fuse although ...irburst fuse is also ...able.

**Cartridge case**

**Receiver group**

**Detonator**

**Trigger guard**

**Trigger**

**Stock assembly**
To remove the stock to clean the working parts in the receiver, remove the screw and washers at the base of the half pistol grip and you can then pull the stock off backwards.

**Stock**

**Sling swivel**

M79 grenadiers put down volley fire on a distant **VC** position after the 'point' of the column had received sniper fire. The aim was to put grenades on and beyond the enemy to keep him pinned down while the assault group put the attack in.

## The 40 mm multiple projectile cartridge

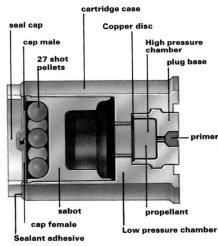

seal cap

cap male

27 shot pellets

cartridge case

Copper disc

High pressure chamber

plug base

primer

sabot

cap female

Sealant adhesive

propellant

Low pressure chamber

This round can be fired from all 40-mm grenade launchers and is intended for close quarter battle and as a rapid response to ambushes. There are two types currently in production: the XM 576 E1 and E2. In the E1 the cartridge case holds a plastic sabot containing a shot cup filled with 20 metal pellets. The sabot and cup are stripped away by air pressure as soon as the shot and sabot reach the muzzle. The E2 is more like a conventional shotgun cartridge as the sabot acts like a shot cup and 27 pellets are carried across the full diameter of the round.

M203 launcher, which has now entirely replaced the M79 in US Army service.

### Pump action weapon

The M203 is a simple tube with a firing mechanism and trigger, clamped to the barrel of the M16 rifle. To load, the barrel is slid forward and a grenade inserted, and the barrel slipped back to lock to the breech. A separate ladder sight is used for aiming the launcher, and the launcher trigger is used to fire it. The advantage is that the rifle is available for use at any time, since neither weapon interferes with the other; the only proviso is that once the launcher is clamped to

*M79 runners were usually positioned well back from the point of a patrol so that they could lob their grenades in without getting directly involved with the fire fight. The HE grenade has a casualty radius of five metres.*

# Battlefield Evaluation: comparing

## M79

The first weapon firing spin-stabilised grenades to enter service, the M79 proved highly successful in Vietnam. Able to provide an infantry section with accurate area fire at up to 400m, in the hands of an experienced grenadier it can put grenades through a window at 150m. Its great limitation is that a man with an M79 cannot carry a rifle as well – US army grenadiers carried .45 pistols. Hence its replacement by the M203, which fits under the barrel.

**Specification:**
**Calibre:** 40mm
**Mode of fire:** break open, single shot
**Barrel length:** 356mm
**Projectile weight:** 227g

**Assessment**
Reliability ★★★★
Accuracy ★★★★
Age ★★★★★
Worldwide users ★★★★

*The M79 is an excellent weapon but after 36 rounds all you're armed with is a pistol.*

## M203

Successfully tested in Vietnam and introduced in time to see considerable service there, the M203 is an exceptionally valuable infantry weapon. The sights are graduated to 400m but experienced troops in Vietnam tended to rely on their judgement and aim by eye alone. A buckshot round is provided, which makes a handy anti-ambush weapon and, of course, the grenadier can now double as a rifleman.

**Specification:**
**Calibre:** 40mm
**Mode of fire:** single-shot pump action
**Barrel length:** 305mm
**Projectile weight:** 227g

**Assessment**
Reliability ★★★★
Accuracy ★★★★
Age ★★★
Worldwide users ★★★★

*The additional firepower of the assault rifle above the M203 makes it a better option.*

## Heckler & Koch HK 79

This M203 style fits the Heckler & Koch G3 and G41 rifles. The barrel drops down to load, which allows you to use rounds of any length: this is an advantage over the M203 which can only use short, low-velocity rounds because of the limits of its forward-sliding movement. The HK 79 is used by the Bundeswehr and the Norwegian army.

**Specification:**
**Calibre:** 40mm
**Mode of fire:** single-shot beneath loading
**Barrel length:** 000mm
**Projectile weight:** 230g

**Assessment**
Reliability ★★★★
Accuracy ★★★★
Age ★★
Worldwide users ★★

*This weapon fires the longer and more powerful grenades that do not fit in the M203.*

the rifle, it needs to be re-zeroed since the clamping and the weight will obviously upset the existing zero.

The 40-mm grenade caught on in many countries and there are several makers of launchers today, some clip-on like the M203 and some handheld like the M79, plus a few oddballs. They all fire the same grenades to the same range and at the same velocity, so choosing between them is simply a matter of cost and preference.

*A grenadier enjoys a meal on a road convoy in South Vietnam. Note the early type HE grenade tucked under the helmet band. These rounds armed between 14 and 28 m, which meant that at close range you had to rely on your .45.*

# grenade launchers

## Heckler & Koch Granatepistole

A light and handy 40-mm grenade launcher, the Granatepistole has an extendable stock, fixed foresight and folding ladder pattern rear sight. The barrel is rifled and the maximum effective range is 400 m. It is loaded by pulling back the cocking handle and breaking open the barrel. The Granatepistole is in service with the Bundeswehr.

**Specification:**
**Calibre:** 40 mm
**Mode of fire:** single-shot break action
**Barrel length:** 356 mm
**Projectile weight:** 230 g

**Assessment**
Reliability ★★★★
Accuracy ★★★★
Age ★★
Worldwide users ★

*The Heckler & Koch launcher is an updated and improved M79.*

## FN telescopic rifle grenade

Grenades fired from the end of a rifle barrel used to require special cartridges which were generally unpopular. Then various firms produced bullet traps, which allow you to fire conventional ball ammunition to launch the grenade without blowing yourself up. FN's unique telescopic grenade allows the bullet to pass *through* the grenade so you can fire AP, incendiary, tracer or whatever else you happen to have loaded. Both 5.56-mm or 7.62-mm rounds can be used.

**Specification:**
**Calibre:** 37 mm
**Mode of fire:** from the rifle muzzle
**Barrel length:** 356 mm
**Projectile weight:** 295 g
**Lethal radius:** 10 m

**Assessment**
Reliability ★★★
Accuracy ★★★
Age ★
Worldwide users ★

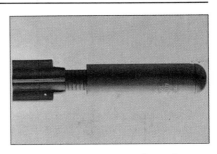

*Rifle grenades can never be quite as accurate as a 40-mm grenade launcher, but they can be fitted to any rifle.*

## AGS-17 automatic grenade-launcher

The US Navy developed an automatic grenade-launcher for patrol boats in Vietnam, and it was later adopted by the army as well. The Soviets introduced a similar weapon in 1975 and several came into Western hands after being captured in Afghanistan. Soviet infantry companies each have two AGS-17s, which can lay down heavy suppressive fire. Maximum effective range is about 1000 m, but it will drop rounds out to 1750 m.

**Specification:**
**Calibre:** 30 mm
**Operation:** blowback
**Feed:** 29-round belt
**Rate of fire:** 65 rounds a minute
**Barrel length:** 290 mm
**Projectile weight:** 275 g

**Assessment**
Reliability ★★★
Accuracy ★★★
Age ★★
Worldwide users ★★★

*The much less portable AGS-17 can provide devastating fire support.*

# Protect yourself with Body Armour

**Like any clothing, body armour has to be chosen according to the nature of the threat. You wouldn't take a parka to the desert, or shorts to the Arctic; in the same way, body armour has been configured according to the climate of violence you will be operating in.** Choose the wrong armour and you won't be hot or cold – you'll be dead.

### Vital organs

In essence, armour is either 'soft' or 'hard' and comes in different lengths and sizes. A mix of soft and hard armour gives protection to vital organs like the heart against high-velocity rounds, while soft armour protects against fragments and low-velocity ammunition.

### Bomb protection

At the extreme end of hard armour is the Explosive Ordnance Device suit (EOD), designed for bomb disposal teams. This consists of a helmet, and body, leg and arm protection in a mix of hard and soft armour. There is a breast plate in hard ceramic material which has a curve designed to deflect blast away from the wearer's face. A cooling system keeps the wearer comfortable and prevents the clear armoured visor from fogging. The major problem with this type of body armour is that the wearer must leave his hands unprotected so that he can handle the explosive to defuse it.

### Bulletproof accessories

One of the lighter and more discreet forms of protection is a bullet-proof clip board, which will stop hits by weapons such as 9-mm .45 and .357 Magnum pistols and shotgun blasts. One of the problems is that the user's hands are exposed, and if a handle is fitted on the other side it looks like a shield and the value of concealment is lost. Bulletproof briefcases are also available.

The average body armour, however, is soft and is designed to cover the wearer from neck to hips, leaving his arms free to handle a weapon, and not weighing too much; three to five kilograms on average. It may include pockets at the back and front to take additional hard armour plating to upgrade the standard of protection.

### Zip problems

Jackets dating back to the Vietnam War that have now come onto the commercial market offer protection against low-velocity ammunition, but not against 5.56-mm rounds. They have a zip and press stud closure, and British soldiers wearing similar jackets in Northern Ireland were instructed to use only the press studs – if the clothing caught fire the nylon in the jacket would melt and the zip would fuse solid.

The pattern of jacket adopted by the US Marines in Vietnam had a band of material at the bottom with eyelets from which equipment could be hung.

## Vital protection

**Artillery remains the 'grim reaper' of the modern battlefield, causing more casualties than any other weapon. In the major conflicts since World War II roughly two-thirds of all combat casualties have been due to the steel fragments produced by exploding shells, bombs and mines. Body armour can offer considerable protection against otherwise lethal shell splinters and many armies now issue it as standard equipment.**

**Head protection**
In Vietnam it was estim that if troops had kept helmets on more regu admissions to the neurosurgical centre w have been reduced by third. Moral: don't mak habit of taking your he off when you think it's

*The US Forces have used body armour on a regular basis since World War II. Here US Air Force security troops watch an airstrike on VC positions outside the perimeter of Tan Son Nhut. They are wearing the old style flak jacket which can now be bought commercially and cheaply.*

*Above right: US Marines in action at Khe Sanh. Their flak jackets have a pad to stop the rifle butt slipping off the shoulder and attachment points for webbing along the bottom. These early armour vests were heavy and opened at the front with a zip and press studs.*

**Searching an enemy position**
Dying soldiers have often been known to lie in their position clutching a grenade with the pin removed, holding the fly off lever down with their body. Troops fighting through the position turn the body over and the grenade explodes, so watch out!

**Booby trap**
Here, members of a US squad have captured an enemy position only to suffer casualties from a grenade trap. If you see a grenade thrown or hear someone shout 'Grenade!' you should take cover immediately.

*A BM21 multiple rocket launcher of the Iraqi army unleashes a storm of explosive and steel splinters on Iranian positions. These weapons are widely used by the Warsaw Pact, making the issue of flak jackets to NATO troops a very sound idea.*

*The result: wounded Iranian soldiers taken prisoner are suffering from multiple fragmentation wounds. Body armour can protect your chest cavity from otherwise fatal damage; wounds to this area are more likely to kill you than hits to peripheral areas.*

**Bullet wounds**
The vest offers a high degree of protection against pistol and sub-machine gun bullets which travel at a much lower velocity than a rifle round. However, although the vest cannot guarantee to stop a rifle bullet, it can convert an otherwise fatal wound into a less serious injury.

**US body armour**
The current issue US Army flak vest seen here is a very solid piece of kit made from Kevlar ballistic cloth. It forms part of PASGT (Personal Armour System Ground Troops) together with the Kevlar helmets.

**PASGT helmet**
Laminated with 18 layers of Kevlar armour, the helmet is designed to stop or deflect shell fragments and low powered bullets. It is substantially stronger than the old steel helmet.

**Flak jackets**
Your flak jacket can mean the difference between life and death. The vest protects your vital organs from shell splinters, pistol and SMG rounds and, in this case, the blast and fragmentation produced by a grenade trap.

**Grenade Immediate Action**
If there is no cover available, hit the ground and roll away from the grenade. Do not try to run to cover: if it goes off while you are standing up you are more likely to be injured.

**Layered armour**
Fragments may penetrate the outer layers of ballistic fabric but are slowed down by multiple layers. Only a large chunk of shell or a very close range blast will have enough velocity left to injure you after it has penetrated the armour.

# Survival

The Israelis in the 1982 invasion of Lebanon took this further by fitting ammunition and equipment pouches directly to their flak jackets. This scheme makes sure that ammunition and jacket are always together, and spreads the load evenly across the shoulders and back.

Modern jackets have a Velcro closure, normally under the arms. This makes alteration for different-sized wearers much easier, leaves no weak lines at the front of the jacket, and allows it to be removed quickly if the wearer needs medical treatment.

Neck protection has become a priority in body armour design – current US and Israeli jackets feature a high collar; when worn with a ballistic helmet this increases the protection for the very vulnerable head and neck. Future developments will certainly include eye protection.

### Discreet protection

Body armour does not have to be obvious. Some patterns are designed to be worn under combat jackets: this has a number of advantages, because in a politically sensitive area 'flak jackets' worn by police or soldiers are inclined to raise the emotional temperature. Also, you will be able to get at the equipment stored in your combat jacket. The disadvantage of discreet protection is that it does not cover your neck or reach down to cover your kidneys and lower abdomen.

The ultimate in discreet body armour are jackets and vests designed for covert police wear or VIP protection. These can be worn under a shirt and are normally in white. Others are cut like a windbreaker or blouson and are in neutral colours, and so can be worn with casual clothes without attracting attention.

### Non-standard wearers

Not all wearers are a standard size. Military protective clothing can be adjusted using the Velcro closures and comes in small, medium and large, but police or civilian clothing needs to be properly sized. One US company has a properly-cut vest to accommodate a bust for female police officers to wear under a shirt. In Northern Ireland an enterprising company produces a wide range of clothing including car coats, corduroy jackets, and even a quilted body warmer.

### Bullet shock

There are mixed opinions about the trauma that the body suffers when it takes the shock from a bullet hitting body armour. Some people maintain that the function of body armour is to stop hits by small arms; others say that

*An EOD engineer in full protection minus helmet looks on as a tertiary explosive (fertiliser and diesel oil) is shovelled out of the boot of a car bomb. The boot was blown open with a remote controlled tractor, Goliath. There are two types of body armour in the photo, two soldiers are wearing the current issue INIBA vest which is worn underneath your combat jacket.*

*Almost any article can be lined with bullet-proof material. Bullet-proof clip boards are in service with a number of police forces, but they do not protect your hands.*

*Combat experience often leads armies to adopt body armour; this is the Israeli system of load-carrying armour. Even the Soviets, not previously very concerned over the lives of their conscripts, are now issuing body armour to their units occupying Afghanistan.*

this is not enough and that the shock and bruising from hits can cause internal damage to the wearer. They advocate a 'trauma pad' – in effect, padding inside the armour – which dissipates the shock. One soldier who took a hit from an Armalite while serving in Northern Ireland survived because the round hit the ceramic plate on the back of his armour, but the bruise was considerable and he was unable to sleep on his back for several days afterwards.

## Foot armour

Armour can extend to the feet: US jungle boots in Vietnam had a plate in the sole to protect the wearer from punji stakes, the sharpened bamboos that would penetrate the foot of an unwary soldier. A modern commercially-marketed boot has Kevlar material in the uppers, though this is intended as protection against indus-

*Left and inset: The forerunner of the INIBA vest was a simple flak vest intended to protect you from shell splinters rather than a sniper's bullet. Inset is the next in line, with added rubber shoulder pads to stop the butt slipping off your shoulder.*

trial injury.

Nomex fire retardant fabric is not regarded as 'armour', but it is a valuable addition to a soldier's protection. Nomex clothing is now used in flying overalls, tank crew clothing and even in gloves. The Israelis issued large amounts of it to their soldiers in 1982 when they invaded Lebanon. Interestingly, it is one type of protection that can be bought second hand in surplus stores, or even unissued through mail order firms.

## Protected flying

US Air Force flying jackets (but not the ones with reversible orange linings) are made from Nomex, and with gloves would give the wearer protection against fuel-generated fires such as those in helicopters or vehicles. Even leather gloves can save your hands in a flash fire, and as long as they do not prevent you from using a weapon they are a simple but sensible precaution.

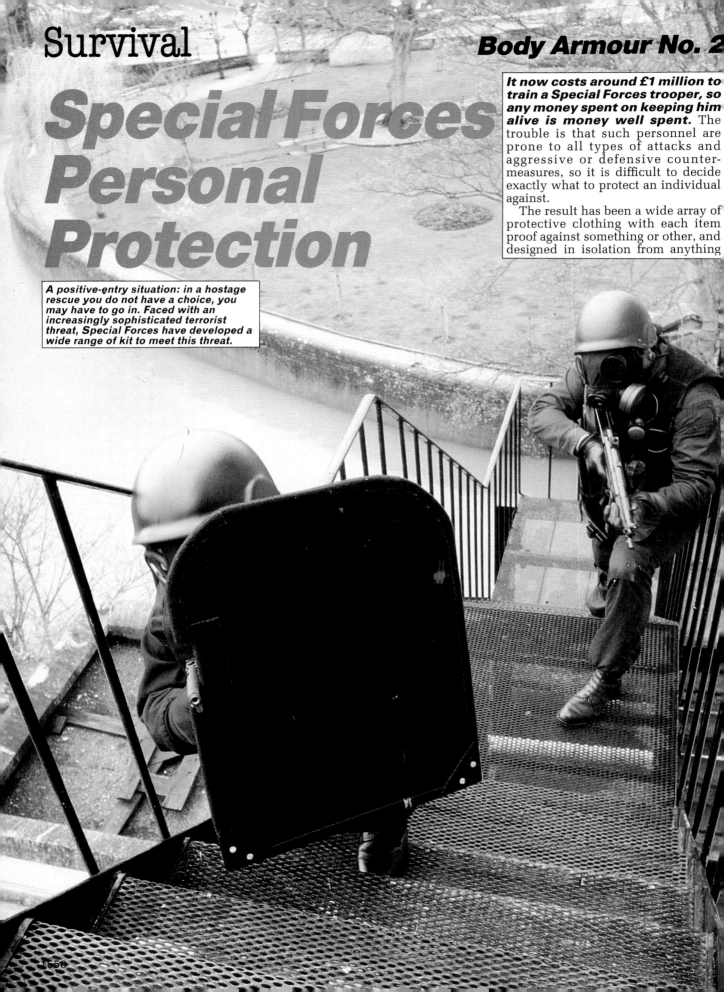

# Special Forces Personal Protection

**It now costs around £1 million to train a Special Forces trooper, so any money spent on keeping him alive is money well spent.** The trouble is that such personnel are prone to all types of attacks and aggressive or defensive counter-measures, so it is difficult to decide exactly what to protect an individual against.

The result has been a wide array of protective clothing with each item proof against something or other, and designed in isolation from anything

*A positive-entry situation: in a hostage rescue you do not have a choice, you may have to go in. Faced with an increasingly sophisticated terrorist threat, Special Forces have developed a wide range of kit to meet this threat.*

**Helmet**
The National Plastics AC 100/1 ballistic composite helmet provides an advanced head protection system for special forces. It is made up of layers of ballistic cloth and will protect the head from a variety of small arms fire as well as blows.

**Headset**
The Davies Communications CT 100 ear protection and communication harness has a body-worn microphone and switching unit with a large press-to-talk button, which can be operated by either hand.

**Respirator**
The Avon Industrial Polymers SF 10 respirator features high levels of protection against incapacitants and low breathing resistance. You can use two canisters or one canister and an air bottle.

**Body armour**
The Armourshield REV777/25 contoured front and back ceramic composite plates, layered Kevlar and blunt trauma shield will defeat high velocity rifle fire.

**Heckler & Koch MP5 sub-machine gun**
The closed bolt design is inherently more accurate than the more simple open bolt models.

**Fire-retardant suit**
This is the GD Specialist Supplies fire retardant body protection system.

# Ballistic helmet

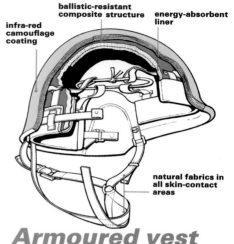

ballistic-resistant composite structure

infra-red camouflage coating

energy-absorbent liner

natural fabrics in all skin-contact areas

# Armoured vest

The Armourshield GPV/25 armoured vest is capable of absorbing a bullet's energy so successfully that the wearer will be able to react. It is a combination of soft Kevlar and hard ceramic plates.

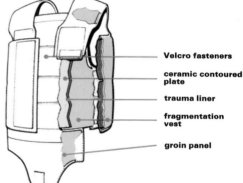

Velcro fasteners

ceramic contoured plate

trauma liner

fragmentation vest

groin panel

else. This often means that when all the various items are worn together they do not integrate: NBC respirator face seals may be broken when a helmet is put on, weapons cannot be sighted through respirator lenses, bulletproof garments interfere with movement, and so on.

This integration problem has been overcome by five British companies which have got together and developed a protective outfit that is proof against most threats to special forces personnel. It is known as the Integrated Personal Protection System (IPPS), and has been tested by Special Forces. The IPPS is not just a design venture: it has been developed using all manner of practical combat experience, and the result is a superb protective outfit.

Starting from the skin outwards, the basis of the IPPS is a set of carbonised viscose 'long john' underwear. The material is light and comfortable to wear but is flame-retardant, as is the main overgarment, a one-piece assault suit also made from carbon fibre material, in this case Nomex 3. The suit incorporates flame retardant pads at the elbows and knees, allowing the wearer to crawl safely over hot surfaces such as aircraft engines during hijack hostage rescue missions.

Incidentally, the suits are very similar to those being worn by tanker crews currently operating in the Persian Gulf, but theirs are coloured bright orange; the IPPS is usually black.

## Flame-retardant

Over the flame-retardant garments the IPPS features a bullet-proof waist-coat made of soft fragmentation armour and with a built-in trauma liner to absorb shock. Without this liner internal injuries could occur even if a bullet is stopped by the

*Special Forces personnel prepare to storm through a doorway. Experience has shown that the third man to enter a building is in the greatest need of body armour because he stands the highest chance of being hit by enemy fire.*

# Survival

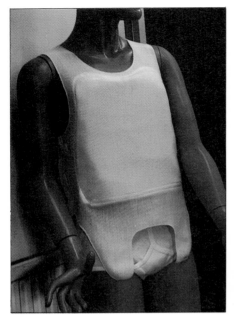

*This Armourshield Ultra Light Undervest concealable body armour with blunt trauma shield weights just over a kilogram: little more than the weight of a bag of sugar.*

*Armourshield FW 25 TF: This is a dual-purpose body armour designed to stop both low velocity fragments and a high-velocity rifle round fired at three metres. The ceramic plates are specially held off the chest to allow unrestricted breathing.*

armour. The soft armour protection is enhanced by inserting curved ceramic plates at the front and back; these can stop 0.357 Magnum bullets at a range of three metres. A groin panel can be added if required.

Further armoured protection is provided by a special helmet known as the AC 100/1, a National Plastics product made from layers of a Kevlar-type material. This can withstand the impact of a 9-mm bullet at close range, and to ensure the wearer's head is not knocked off by the impact, the helmet uses a bullet trauma lining.

An optional fire-retardant leather waistcoat can be worn over the suit and armour protection, and is used to carry special equipment such as an assault axe, stun grenades or rescue knife, all in specially-fitted pockets or leather loops.

These days some form of respirator is worn operationally by most special forces, so the IPPS uses a specially-developed respirator known as the SF10, a variant of the Avon S10 used

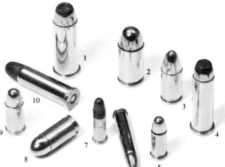

*Above: The threat, (1) 44 Magnum; (2) .45 ACP; (3) 9-mm; (4) .357 magnum; (5) 6.35-mm; (6) .22 Magnum; (7) .22LR; (8) 9-mm Short; (9) 7.65-mm (10) .38 Special.*

*Left: This shows the effect of a .357 Magnum fired at Plasticine protected by a vest with and without a blunt trauma shield.*

by the British Army. The SF10 has an internal microphone, but its most prominent features are the outset darkened eyepieces. These have been incorporated to cut down the flash produced by stun grenades or other bright lights. The SF10 can also be fitted with its own air supply from an air bottle carried in the leather waistcoat or an extra filter canister can be worn.

## Assault team

The respirator microphone connects into an assault team communications harness known as the CT 100, which has a chest or respirator microphone and press-to-talk switches located on the wrist or anywhere handy. The communications system uses electronic earphones that are designed to cut out sound produced by grenades or gunfire (i.e. high air pressure) but which allow all other sounds to be heard normally. The earphones are connected into the communication harness to allow the wearer to listen in to a team command net.

The main feature of the IPPS is that all the components are designed to work together. For instance, the IPPS helmet does not interfere with the respirator seal, and the ear defenders fit under helmet ear lobes that have been

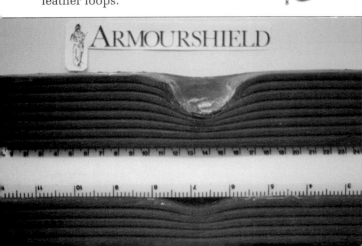

designed for just that purpose. The darkened eyepieces permit almost any weapon to be aimed and fired without difficulty, and even though the protective waistcoat can stop most fragments or bullets it still allows complete freedom of movement.

## Belt kit

A belt carrying combat or other gear can be worn, and an abseiling harness has been developed for use with the IPPS, which provides an indication of the degree of movement available.

The IPPS is not cheap, but considering the cost of training special forces personnel and the fact that their operational missions are very often 'one-offs' where not everything can be anticipated, the costs involved appear to be well worth consideration. Perhaps its most important 'selling feature' is that it has been designed and developed by people who know only too well the problems involved with such equipment and the situations in which the IPPS is used.

*Right: The US solution – high-risk modular tactical armour developed by Point Blank with LAPD SWAT units (Special Weapons And Tactics). The armour has a number of separate load-bearing removable pouches. Construction is of Kevlar with pockets for up-armour plates.*

*The Iranian Embassy Siege. In this situation you need a high level of protection whilst still being able to move fast and use your weapons; this requires an exceptional level of fitness.*

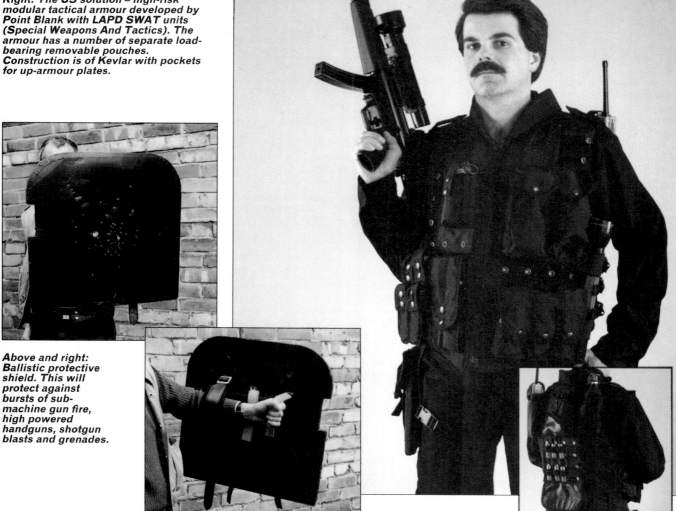

*Above and right: Ballistic protective shield. This will protect against bursts of sub-machine gun fire, high powered handguns, shotgun blasts and grenades.*

# Personal Camouflage and Concealment

*Good camouflage and fieldcraft are almost as important as good marksmanship — in fact, a well-camouflaged man who is a poor shot will probably survive longer than the badly-concealed sniper.*
In an escape and evasion operation, camouflage and concealment are paramount. The hunted man will con-

*Remember your legs when adding local vegetation to break up your shape, but don't add too much foliage here or you will trip up.*

*When you sort out your camouflage leave your rifle resting on your webbing, out of the mud. Make sure the foliage you use matches the area you will be moving through.*

ceal himself and sleep by day, and move by night — and here even the cover of darkness will not negate the importance of camouflage.

Personal camouflage (PC) has certain simple rules that will defeat the most obvious sensor on the battlefield — the human eye.

### Shape

Your helmet, web equipment, rifle and other kit such as manpack radios have a clear, often square shape — and there are no squares in nature. Break up straight lines by the addition of scrim — neutral-coloured strips of cloth in browns and greens. Camouflaged elasticated pack covers exist, and these can be stretched over packs and radios.

Rifles and LMG/GPMGs have a clear shape, and are often black. Though scrim can be used to break up their line, it is not advisable to fix it to the stock — it may slip when you are firing and by shifting your grip cause you to shoot inaccurately. It is better to cover the weapon with camouflaged tape, or

even green masking tape (tape is a useful aid to PC – see **'Sound'**)

A discarded vehicle camouflage net is a very useful source of camouflage for PC. It will have nylon 'scrim' that has been treated to give an infra-red reflection similar to vegetation. Fixed to the back of packs and webbing, or in the netting on a helmet, it breaks up shape very well and enhances the chlorophyll-based infra-red camouflage treatment. (see also **'Silhouette'**).

### Shine

In the old days of brass buckles, soldiers were told these should be allowed to grow dull, or be covered with masking tape. However, most web equipment has plastic or alloy fittings that do not reflect – but there are still shiny surfaces even on a modern battlefield.

Binoculars and compass surfaces, even spectacles, can catch the light. There is little that can be done about spectacles, but when using binoculars or a compass make sure that you are well concealed: like radios, they are 'signature equipment' and attract attention. Stow binoculars inside your smock, and take care that your map is not opened up and flapping about – a drab map case with the map folded so that it gives the minimum

*Use everything that comes to hand: in this case, a bit of discarded vehicle camouflage net which helps blur the shape of your kit.*

**Too much**
*The 'walking bush' looks effective at first sight, but he has so much foliage over his webbing he cannot get at his ammunition.*

**Too little**
*The white face and hands reflect the light and stand out horribly, and the lack of foliage reveals the obvious shape of the human figure.*

**Just right**
*Proper camouflage breaks up your shape and dulls the skin areas but does not restrict your access to your webbing or block your vision.*

working area is all that is needed. Take care also that the clear cover to the map case does not catch the light.

Shine also includes skin. At night it will catch moonlight and flares, and even black soldiers need to use camouflage cream.

## Silhouette

Similar in many respects to shape, silhouette includes the outline

*By adding more vegetation to your shoulder straps you can hide the familiar 'head and shoulders' shape of the human figure.*

of the human form and the equipment it is carrying. The shape of the head and shoulders of a man are unmistakable and an unscrimmed helmet attracts attention.

The use of vegetation as garnishing helps break up the silhouette. Thick handfuls of grass tucked into equipment can remove the shape of the shoulders, and garnishing on the helmet breaks the smooth curve of the

*The man with too much camouflage must sit up in order to see through the jungle on his helmet but the soldier on the right blends in well.*

top and the line of the brim.

Silhouette also includes fieldcraft – however well camouflaged you may be, it is little help if you 'sky line' by walking along the top of a hill, or stand against a background of one solid colour.

# FACIAL CAMOUFLAGE

**1 The first coat**
First, get rid of all that white, shining skin. Mix a small quantity of camouflage cream with spit in your hand and rub it all over your face, neck and ears. This gives a full light coverage of camouflage. Then cover your hands with the cream.

**2 Breaking up the shape**
Now break up the outline and shape of the eyes, nose and mouth. Any pattern that breaks up this familiar format will do: use more if you're going on night patrol. Don't forget your neck and ears.

**3 Finishing off**
Fill in the rest of your face with earth, loam and green colours, then spit in your hands and rub them over your face to blur it all together. On the move you will probably sweat heavily, so you must top up your face cream as you go along.

Proper stowage of kit, taping of slings and other noisy equipment and a final shakedown before a patrol moves out will reduce noise. If a position is being dug, sentries should be positioned at the limit of noise so that they can see an enemy before he hears the digging.

## Colour

Though most modern combat uniforms are now in a disruptive pattern camouflage, there may be times when this is less helpful. If you are evading

## Smell

Even the most urbanised man will develop a good sense of smell after a few days in the open. He will be able to detect engine smells, cooking, body odour and washing.

Some smells are hard to minimise. Soaps should be scent-free and activities such as cooking confined to daylight hours when other smells are stronger and the air warmer.

One of the greatest giveaways is smoking: its refuse has a unique smell. Rubbish produced by cooking as well as smoking should be carried out from the operational area and only buried as a second choice: buried objects are often dug up by animals and this can give a good indication of the strength and composition of your patrol or unit as well as its morale. The disciplines of refuse removal are important.

## Sound

You can make a lot of noise while out on patrol. Your boots can squeak, your cleaning kit or magazines may rattle in your ammunition pouches. Even your webbing can creak if it is heavy. Fittings on your weapon may rattle. Radios can have background 'mush'. Coughing and talking can carry for long distances in the darkness of a clear night.

You must become familiar with a 'silent routine' in which field signals replace the spoken word, or conversations are conducted in a whisper.

*Right: Personal camouflage must be secured so that it does not shift about when you are running.*

*Below: The familiar round shape of the helmet is broken up and the man's back and shoulders blend in well, but note how an uncamouflaged rifle stands out: there are no straight lines in nature.*

# HELMET CAMOUFLAGE

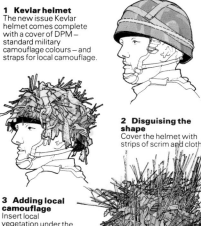

**1 Kevlar helmet**
The new issue Kevlar helmet comes complete with a cover of DPM – standard military camouflage colours – and straps for local camouflage.

**2 Disguising the shape**
Cover the helmet with strips of scrim and cloth.

**3 Adding local camouflage**
Insert local vegetation under the elastic. Use plenty, make sure it stays in, and make sure it matches your background.

# CAMOUFLAGING YOUR RIFLE

Camouflage the stock and butt with pieces of DPM material from an old pair of combat trousers. Make sure nothing gets in the way of the sights and check that you can load, make ready, and change the gas regulator setting easily. Secure the DPM material with tape and strips of cloth. Tie strips of cloth on the fore end and the barrel too, to disguise the overall shape and outline of the rifle. Green or camouflage tape on the magazine and top cover completes the job.

capture and are unarmed, drab civilian outdoor clothing will be less conspicuous if you encounter civilians.

The trouble with camouflage-type clothing is that in the wrong environment, like cities, it seems to do the opposite and say 'Hey, look at me!' In fighting in built-up areas a camouflage of greys, browns and dull reds would be better. The use of sacking and empty sand bags as scrim covers would help here.

Natural vegetation used to garnish helmets and equipment (see 'Silhouette') will fade and change colour. Leaves curl up and show their pale under-surfaces. You may have put

grass into your helmet band and now find yourself in a dark wood; or be wearing dark green ferns when you are moving across a patch of pale, open grass land. Check and change your camouflage regularly.

The most obvious colour that needs camouflaging is that of human skin, and for that you need camouflage cream. As mentioned, even black or brown skin has a shine to it. A common mistake is to smear paint over the front of the face and to miss the neck, ears and back of the hands.

Camouflage cream needs to be renewed as you move and sweat. A simple pattern is to take stripes diagonally across the face – this cuts through the vertical and horizontal lines of the eyes, nose and mouth. Some camouflage creams have two colours, in which case you can use the dark colour to reduce the highlights formed by the bridge of the nose, cheek bones, chin and forehead. The lighter colour is used on areas of shadow.

## Association

The enemy may not see you, but he might spot your equipment or refuse and associate that with a possible unit on the move. A cluster of radio antennas shows that a company HQ is on the move or dug in. The cans stacked near a vehicle park, perhaps with white tape around them, are likely to

*Royal Marines prepare for the landings at San Carlos. Even at night your skin must be camouflaged because it will reflect moonlight.*

be fuel. To a trained observer the unusual – a flash from a plastic map case, or the smell of cooking – will alert him and he will bring his own sensors to bear on the area.

# CAMOUFLAGING YOUR BODY & EQUIPMENT

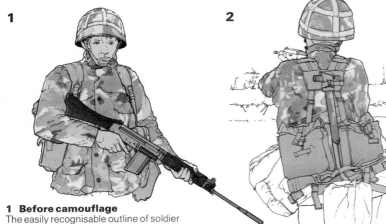

**1**

**2**

**3**

**1  Before camouflage**
The easily recognisable outline of soldier and equipment. Think SHAPE, SHADOW, SHINE, SURFACE and use it as a checklist. Areas to concentrate on are the shapes of your helmet, rifle and 58 pattern webbing; shadow underneath your helmet; and shine from your rifle and digging tool.

**2  How to do it**
Sew elastic strips on your webbing to hold local camouflage. Put your spade in a sandbag: it doesn't just shine, it also makes noise! Attach a camouflage net on a piece of

sacking to your shoulders, to cover the whole of your back. This, like your helmet, should be covered with strips of DPM material.

**3  After camouflage**
The complete picture, with local camouflage secured on equipment and the body with black elastic. It must be secure enough not to fall out when you move or go for cover.

# Hitting the Beach

*Right: The French forces deployed to Lebanon included large numbers of Marine personnel. Their intended role corresponds closely with that of the Royal Marine Commandos: a powerful and balanced amphibious force.*

*Below: AML-90s come ashore from an elderly tank landing craft. L9096 was lent to Lebanon during 1983 but was subsequently returned to French service and is based at Lorient.*

**The 9th Marine Infantry Division (La 9e D.I.Ma) has inherited the traditions of the 9th Commando Infantry Division and is a well equipped, highly motivated and professional formation specialising in amphibious operations.** It cannot be compared with the US Marine Corps or the Royal Marines; it is not a separate Marine Corps but is part of the French army and wears its uniforms and insignia. It is not commando-trained, and therefore does not wear a green beret. Although the division is comprised of marine-orientated troops, it functions as a conventional infantry organisation.

The division has a strength of some 8,000 men, not including the headquarters and training staff, and comprises more than 60 per cent professional 'marine' soldiers, the remainder being conscripts. The professional soldiers are spread throughout the division to provide a stable base into which the conscripts can integrate. This method works well and

*Below: Sixty per cent of the 8,000 men of the 9th Marine Infantry Division are career soldiers with the conscripts spread throughout the formation. The division is motorised and air-transportable as well as amphibious.*

maintains a very mobile and efficient quick-reaction force, able to be air- or sea-lifted to an operational area. Once on land and in action the force is motorised, with more than 2,000 vehicles of various types at its disposal.

The division is centred around four regiments of motorised infantry with principal operational support provided by the 2nd and 3rd Marine Infantry Regiments. These regiments were formed in 1979 and have an operational role of undertaking foreign training missions and provid-

ing specialist operational support.

Heavy firepower for support and reconnaissance is provided by one light armoured regiment, which has an inventory of 36 AML 90s and 26 AML 60s. The AML 90 is a wheeled light armoured car with a number of variants, including one with a 90-mm gun. The AML 60 is a smaller vehicle and in its standard fit is equipped with a 60-mm mortar and twin 7.62-mm machine-guns. One artillery regiment equipped with three batteries of 105-mm howitzers provides fire support and an air defence battery with 30-mm and 40-mm automatic cannon deals with the air threat.

## Self-supporting unit

The support command regiment consists of a surgical unit, which has full forward hospital facilities and is entirely air-transportable, and a medical outpost which is air-portable, either by fixed-wing aircraft or helicopters. This regiment also provides detachments of beach marines, who are responsible for the beach-head during an amphibious landing and provide communications between the beach master, the landing craft and landing ships.

Like all modern amphibious combat groups, the division has to be self-supporting once landed on an enemy beach. It has armoured fighting vehicles, artillery and air support from fixed-wing aircraft and helicopters from the French air force and navy. It has also developed and expanded its anti-tank capability, for it has been

seen that modern anti-tank weapons are not only able to destroy enemy armour but also to neutralise bunkers.

The principal vessels used for amphibious operations are the landing vessels (TCDs) *Ouragan* and *Orage*, which entered service in 1965 and 1967 respectively. They both belong to the Atlantic squadron of the French navy and have similar capabilities. The essential characteristic of the TCDs is the interior 'bowl', called the *'radier'*, which is a dock and can be flooded to a depth of three metres.

A stern door allows access to the open sea, where a variety of landing craft and amphibious vehicles can be dispatched or gathered in for landing and offloading.

For combined seaborne and heliborne operations, the vessels are able to operate both Super Frelon and Puma helicopters. The two vessels are well known to members of the division and to those of the Foreign Legion who use them regularly. Although they are dated, they will serve until the three new TCDs come into service.

*In 1984 the Regiment d'Infanterie de Chars de Marine of the 9th Marine Infantry Division became the first French unit to receive the Panhard ERC Sagaie 6×6 recce vehicle, which performs a similar role to British Scorpions and Scimitars.*

*The ERC 90 weighs little over eight tonnes, making it air-transportable, but its 90-mm gun gives it superior firepower to cannon-armed armoured cars and enables it to engage older MBTs. Optional kit includes NBC system, ground navigation compass and air conditioning.*

*Firing the 81-mm mortar: this provides the bulk of the Marine Infantry Division's integral fire support, although many options, including 155-mm guns, are under consideration.*

began as 'B' Company, 2nd Fusilier battalion of the Belgian army was attached to the British Parachute Regiment and by 1944 became a squadron in the SAS.

The modern Belgian Paracommandos are divided into green-bereted commandos and red-bereted paratroopers, but they undergo the same training and are all airborne-qualified. French and Belgian officers often serve on attachment with each other's units and the Belgian Paracommandos undertake specialist courses such as HALO parachuting, combat swimming, demolitions and mountain and winter warfare in France.

France maintains a powerful overseas intervention force including amphibious, airborne and mountain troops. Without its influence it is highly doubtful whether the British forces would have been able to recapture the Falklands in 1982. Six years earlier, the French landed troops in Kolwezi, halting the massacre of Europeans and locals by tribal rebels. Only then did it dawn on the British government that the reduction in the British Army's airborne strength left our forces incapable of such an operation. Subsequent reorganisation was only just in time.

During the Indo-China war (1946-54) France committed considerable forces, which included elements of the Marine Infantry who fought alongside other elite formations such as the French paras and Foreign Legion. In the 1956 Suez crisis three Marine units and a force of Legionnaires made a seaborne landing at Port Foud as part of the British and French intervention force. The operation was a total success and, like the British Royal Marines, displayed the ability to mobilise and land an amphibious force at relatively short notice.

### Marines in Algeria

One of the most controversial French military conflicts in the postwar years was the Algerian war of independence. At the peak of the fighting against the ALN (Armée de Liberation Nationale), the French forces numbered 300,000 troops, most of whom were deployed in a series of garrisons across Algeria. Strikes against the ALN were carried out by the Reserve Générale, which comprised some 30,000 crack troops of the Marine Infantry, Paras and Legion. Members of the Marine Infantry have since found themselves on operations in Chad where Colonel Gaddafi had intervened in the civil war. The French Marines also provide resident battalions in the African countries of Gabon, Ivory Coast, Dakar and Senegambia.

The French amphibious forces have very close links with the Belgian Paracommandos and they often train together. Like the French, the Belgian Paracommandos can trace their ancestry back to World War II, when soldiers who had escaped to Britain formed a small army in exile. What

*Above the 6e Division Légère Blindée (6th light armoured division) provides a powerful mechanised element to the French overseas intervention force. The VAB with HOT anti-tank missiles can kill MBTs at up to 4,000 m.*

*Below: Belgian Paracommandos work closely with the French amphibious forces. Like the French special forces, they were created during World War II as part of the Allied commando forces organised by the SAS.*

# Combat Report
## Lebanon:
# Bodyguards in Beirut

**A Close Protection Officer working in Beirut describes a terrorist attack that he encountered while protecting a political VIP.**

When we were looking after VIPs we usually wore suits and carried 9-mm pistols which were kept out of view of the public. On this occasion, because of the high risk of attack from terrorist organisations, the order of the day was jeans and T-shirts, carrying M16s, with Browning high-power 9-mm hand guns strapped to our sides. Anyone who has worked in this type of environment will tell you that this form of operation is psychologically tiring — continuously checking every window, street corners, passing motor vehicles and a thousand and one other places from where an attack could suddenly spring. Apart from the obvious threats, there was also the booby-trap and car bomb to watch for. A few days previously, a terrorist had driven a lorry packed with explosives into the compound of the American Embassy.

Due to the political status of the VIP we were protecting, there was a good possibility that we, too, would come under such a kamikaze attack. Because our team was all British, there was a possibility that even we could be kidnapped and held hostage. After three Russian diplomats had been abducted in the city some months previously, the KGB forced the terrorists to release the men within 24 hours. This was achieved quite simply but in a most horrific manner: the leader's four sons had been kidnapped, one of them was killed, the head severed and delivered to his father. Pinned to the head was a note to the effect that if the men were not released within a stipulated time, the remaining three heads would follow. Before this incident had taken place, we had already decided that if one of our mates was to be captured, decisive action would be needed to force their release.

## Well-armed amateurs

One morning, against our professional advice, our VIP insisted on attending a meeting in the west of the city. To escort him to his destination we used three Range Rovers, with the VIP travelling in the centre vehicle. All went well until we entered an area of the city that had been bombed several months earlier. Most of the high rise residential blocks were now just piles of rubble, and buildings that still stood showed the scars of bullet and rocket attacks. Suddenly, the road exploded in front of us as an RPG-7 just missed the leading vehicle. Immediately, we went into our anti-ambush drill, with men from the front and rear vehicles giving covering fire whilst the escorts manhandled the VIP from the centre vehicle, throwing him behind a pile of rubble. When he was safely settled, they were then quickly joined by the rest of the team.

A quick evaluation of the situation showed that the enemy were well-armed amateurs. Although some of their fire was accurate, it became apparent that most of the gunmen were just frantically blasting off with their automatic weapons in our general direction. We were out-numbered and it was obvious that the opposition had an abundance of ammunition at their disposal. The only way that we were going to win this fire fight was by using swift, skilful tactics and accurate, concentrated fire.

Approximately 50 yards in front of us we could clearly see two men with AK47s. They had their fingers permanently on the triggers, letting off a magazine at a time. The climbing

effect of the recoil caused the bullets to fly way above our heads, ricocheting off the surrounding rubble. Dave Bradley and Roger Taylor manoeuvred towards the terrorists, using fire and movement. Their assault on the position and the fast, accurate fire clearly shocked the two terrorists. In the meantime, the rest of the team were exchanging shots with other terrorists as they were glimpsed amongst the rubble. Suddenly, there was a loud booming noise as rubble and brick dust rained down on us and a large dust cloud lingered in the air — one of the terrorists was using a rocket launcher.

As the terrorist prepared to fire again, Pete Holland was already waiting for him to raise his head above the cover of bricks. A single shot from Pete's M16 killed him instantly. Dave and Roger were now fighting a close-quarter battle amongst the mountains of rubble that had once been high rise flats. Three men were left to protect the VIP as the rest of us manoeuvred forward to join the fire fight. Slowly edging our way, with our weapons at the ready, we used the traditional CQB method of double-tap fire and movement. As soon as a terrorist came into sight, we fired two shots then made for cover. Pete and I saw one terrorist at exactly the same moment. He was only a matter of a few feet away but, before I could fire, Pete had already nailed him. The action was fast and furious, with no time to think, we just acted on our well-trained instincts. Suddenly, a terrorist stumbled across Dave Hedges. They were only a few feet apart and the startled terrorist began to raise his AKM. Dave, a veteran of many campaigns, had the advantage as his military pump-action shotgun was already in the 'ready' position. As the terrorist fell, it seemed as if that was the signal for the fighting to stop: his uninjured colleagues seemed to melt away as if by magic.

In the quiet that followed the cessation of firing, we heard a whimpering noise coming

**Above: The greatest threat to our VIP was from an assassin who had acquired an RPG-7 anti-tank rocket like this one carried by a Syrian soldier.**

from behind a semi-demolished wall. There, I found a man cowering in the corner of the rubble, with an AKM lying at his side. One of the lads who spoke the language discovered that he was the leader of this group and, because of our fighting skills, he had thought we were the KGB. Bob Carlton, who I must admit has a more than unusual sense of humour, told the frightened terrorist leader that we were ex-British Special Forces. This seemed to relieve him somewhat until Bob added "the KGB learnt their tactics from us". From that day on, we had no further problems with that or any associated terrorist groups.

**Below: They love posing for the camera, but these militiamen were not prepared for a serious fight with our well-trained team.**

# Fighting Fit

# INTO THE HILLS

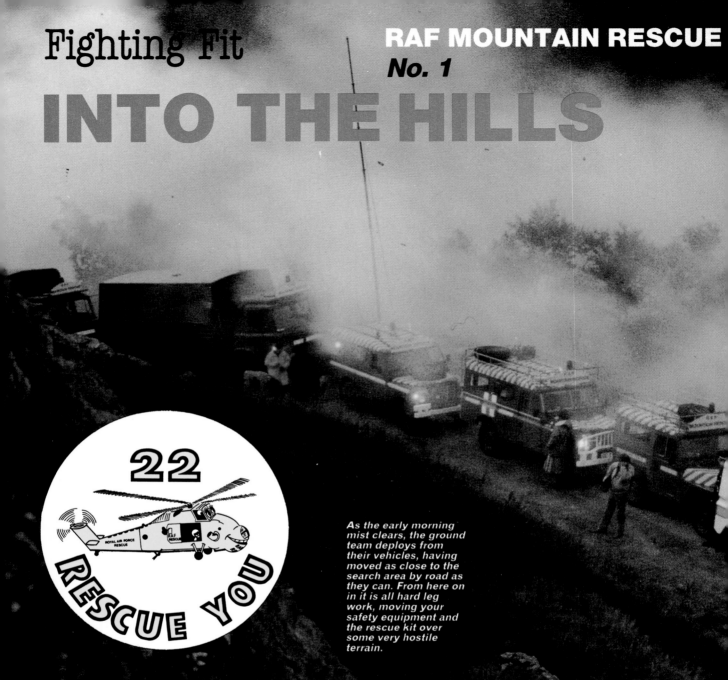

**22 RESCUE YOU**

*As the early morning mist clears, the ground team deploys from their vehicles, having moved as close to the search area by road as they can. From here on in it is all hard leg work, moving your safety equipment and the rescue kit over some very hostile terrain.*

**Late October, and the weather was turning colder as it grew dark, though Snowdonia is no place to be caught out after dark in any season.** The three hikers were already in trouble. None of them was properly dressed or equipped for the mountains, and they had underestimated the sheer hard work of mountain walking. Tired, and without adequate boots, the woman had slipped, fallen, and sprained her ankle, and now she was immobile. One of the men stayed with her, while the other set off on the long trek down to get help. By the time he reached a phone box the evening was drawing in, and the man who had stayed behind, wearing thin, sweat-damp clothing, was in the first stages of hypothermia.

As soon as the police message came through to RAF Valley, in Anglesey, the Mountain Rescue Unit contacted the duty Search and Rescue crew of C Flight, 22 Squadron in their ops room on the other side of the sprawling camp. It was a typical incident for both teams. By the time the SAR Wessex helicopter reached the scene of the accident the two casualties were hidden by cloud. The MR section and the helicopter's winchman were dropped on the hillside just below the cloud base, and soon found the two hikers, administered on-the-spot first aid and then brought them down below the cloud level where they could be picked up by the Wessex and flown to safety. Both the Mountain Rescue Team and the Search and Rescue flight at RAF Valley can, and

*Pilot error, equipment failure and appalling weather cause air crashes in these remote areas every year. The RAF Mountain Rescue is responsible for rescuing civil as well as military aircrew.*

often do, operate independently, but their pooled skills bring unmatchable professional teamwork to the difficult and dangerous tasks they undertake.

**Above: The RAF Search and Rescue was originally formed to rescue RAF aircrew crashed in the mountains during World War II. This is the wreckage of a WWII bomber left as a memorial to its crew.**

**Left: The Wessex helicopter is the workhorse of No. 22 Squadron and provides the eyes of the rescue teams. It can effect a rescue itself, sometimes winching injured climbers from isolated ledges.**

RAF Valley is home to one of the six RAF Mountain Rescue Teams placed strategically around the British Isles. The others are at St Athan in South Wales, Stafford in the West Midlands, Leeming in the North-East, and Leuchars and Kinloss in Scotland. The RAF's Mountain Rescue Service is staffed entirely by volunteers, nearly all of whom have other full-time service jobs. Their rescue work is unpaid and, for the most part, unsung.

## Love for the mountains

At Valley their trades are various – storeman, wireless mechanic, airframe fitter, clerk – but what they all have in common is a single-minded commitment to the difficult and dangerous work of mountain rescue, reinforced by a love of the mountains

and an exuberant sense of comradeship. They jokingly call themselves "the RAF's S.A.S. – we work Saturdays and Sundays". For no extra pay, and no incentive beyond their love of the job, every team member has to pledge to attend a minimum of three weekend exercises and briefings every month.

Originally organised during World War II to help deal with crashed aircraft and casualty-evacuation from difficult terrain, the first group of volunteers operated out of RAF Llandwrog, near Caernarfon, rescuing 22 aircrew from a total of 36 crashes in the first year. The RAF still has responsibility, along with the civilian police, for all crashed aircraft in the country, whether military or civilian. MR teams work with SAR squadrons under the control of the Rescue Co-ordination Centres at Edinburgh and Plymouth. An average of 18 RAF aircraft are lost each year in incidents, and MR units are charged with the job of securing and safeguarding wreckage as well as evacuating casualties, usually in league with SAR helicopters.

SAR helicopter flights of 22 Squadron (Wessex) and 202 Squadron (Sea King) alternate around the British coast. C Flight, at RAF Valley, has two Wessex aircraft attended by four crews, operating 24-hour shifts, with a second crew always on call in case both helicopters are required. In 1987 they attended 12 military incidents and 125 civilian incidents. Their primary official task is to look after NATO military aircraft, and personnel are exchanged with NATO aircrew members from other countries, giving experience in other aircraft and conditions. Most of Valley SAR's calls are

within 20 miles of the home base, and 95 percent of them are civilian. These vary enormously, from holidaymakers on surfboards and inflatable mattresses in the grip of tide and wind, to climbers stuck on sea-cliffs, fishing boats sinking in the Irish Sea, and casualties needing swift evacuation from lifeboats to mainland hospitals. C Flight's longest trip out in 1987 was, unusually, to a French fishing boat off the west of Ireland to transfer a heart attack patient to hospital. Normally a Sea King flight would handle long dis-

**A stretcher party moves a casualty down the mountain. This is exhausting work, and you practise it to ensure you can maintain speed during changeover as the men are rotated through the stretcher party.**

**Sea cliff climbing is uniquely dangerous as climbers cannot retreat once in difficulty as the tide comes in. If the climber falls in a particularly isolated position a helicopter may be the only way off.**

tance over-water operations, having a greater range, as well as radar and an automatic hover facility. For large-scale sea searches, Nimrod aircraft would be called in.

The C Flight Wessex helicopters each have a crew of three – pilot, navigator and winchman. The winchman is trained in First Aid, and is sometimes left with casualties, being lowered if necessary by the navigator, who takes over his function. Helicopters have revolutionised mountain rescue, which was once characterized by long, back-breaking evacuation carries by stretcher and foot. Helicopters can also ferry MR teams high into the terrain of an incident, saving hours of precious time and wearying leg-work. Yet ultimately, if light and weather conditions make helicopter involvement impossible, the MRT can still reach any location overground in any conditions.

The ops rooms of both SAR and MRT are in radio contact with police, ambulance control, lifeboat, and civilian MR units, as well as with their own Rescue Co-ordination Controls and military networks. Sometimes, in bad weather, the police will relay information direct to the helicopter. RAF SAR stations are at Chivenor (Wessex), Brawdy (Sea King), Valley (Wessex), Lossiemouth (Sea King), Leuchars (Wessex), Boulmer (Sea King), Leconfield (Wessex), Coltishall (Sea King), Manston (Wessex). They also liaise with Royal Naval Sea King units at Culdross, Prestwick and Portland.

Friday night. RAF Valley's MRT is going on exercise from a base – an ATC hut – at Bethesda on the mainland. They have reached the base in a convoy of Land Rovers, marked with distinctive yellow chevrons on bonnet and roof, blue roof lights and "RAF Mountain Rescue" headboards above the windscreens. A four-tonner packs most of the gear, including large supplies of food. Mountaineering is hungry work. The local police arrive with tonight's scenario.

## Missing walker

A walker is missing, having set off from Bethesda for Moel Winion, a peak behind the town. He was due back at 4 pm, and it's now 8 pm, dark and clear, with some rain in the air. Edinburgh control is informed of the task and location. If a real emergency crops up, the team will already be in the field and available to act or to be ferried on-site. A stretcher party stays behind, ready for call-up if necessary. Three parties of three men each kit up for the search. Each team has a radio and pyros for signalling (colour flares) and illuminating (paralumes). Party leaders are equipped with headlamps. Each man carries a day-pack containing sleeping bag and bivvy bag, extra clothing, and waterproofs. Conditions can change very fast, and the team is always equipped to stay out for up to 36 hours at a time. One party follows the walker's intended route, ready to return along it if necessary. One party will scale the hill above the town of Aber, and then drop back into the valley along obvious escape routes. The third party does the same along routes to the other side of Moel Winion.

The parties sweep upwards onto the hillsides, using re-entrants. At first it is very marshy, but soon becomes steeper, with large rocks, dark masses of furze, and deep, narrow streams. The teams are marked by the leaders' headlights, sweeping the way ahead, checking the maps. Radio contact is kept up, indicating movements, giving map references. One hour. Two hours. No joy. At intervals they fire off paralumes which float downwind, lighting up the hillsides before abruptly darkening out. Eventually, at a pre-arranged time, the "walker" sets off a strobe marker light. The flashing blue-white light can be seen for miles. He's on a secondary peak already swept by one of the parties. It is all too easy to miss a casualty even in these "good" conditions.

They debrief back at base. The team leader talks through the search, suggesting that sometimes it's easier to let a lost man find you than you find him. Use lights, flares, shouts, so long as there's no ambiguity. It's an early night. Tomorrow terrain and conditions are going to be a lot harder.